TIMSS MONOGRAPH NO. 1

Curriculum Frameworks for Mathematics and Science

David F. Robitaille   Curtis Mc Knight
William H. Schmidt   Edward Britton
Senta Raizen   Cynthia Nicol

GENERAL EDITOR, DAVID F. ROBITAILLE

PACIFIC EDUCATIONAL PRESS

VANCOUVER   CANADA

Copyright © 1993 TIMSS
ISBN 0-88865-090-6
First printing 1993

Pacific Educational Press
Faculty of Education
University of British Columbia
Vancouver, B.C.
Canada V6T 1Z4
Telephone: (604) 822-5385
Fax: (604) 822-6603

Financial support for the International Coordinating Centre for
TIMSS has been provided by the following agencies: National
Center for Education Statistics, U.S. Department of Education, U.S.
National Science Foundation, Employment & Immigration Canada,
Industry, Science & Technology Canada, British Columbia
Ministry of Education, and the International Association for the
Evaluation of Educational Achievement.

Canadian Cataloguing in Publication Data
Main entry under title:

Curriculum frameworks for mathematics and
    science

   (TIMSS monograph ; no. 1)
   Include bibliographical references.
   ISBN 0-88865-090-6

   1. Mathematics--Study and teaching. 2.
Science--Study and teaching. I. Robitaille,
David F. II. Series
QA11.C87 1993   375.5   C93-091833-9

Design: Warren Clark
Printed and bound in Canada

Contents

Preface

This is the first in a series of monographs that will be published through the International Coordinating Centre for the Third International Mathematics and Science Study (TIMSS) at the University of British Columbia. Over the lifetime of the project, we expect that there may be as many as 15 to 20 titles in the series, and our goal is to publish monographs at the rate of two or more each year beginning in 1994. It is appropriate that the first monograph focuses on the TIMSS curriculum frameworks, since those frameworks are the basis upon which the entire structure of the study rests.

Work on the mathematics curriculum framework for TIMSS began in 1989, under the terms of a grant from the British Columbia Ministry of Education. Jane Swafford, Mary Montgomery-Lindquist, and I did the initial work, focusing to a large extent on the development of a methodology for conducting analyses of mathematics textbooks. Graduate students at Illinois State University and the University of British Columbia carried out some preliminary analyses of textbooks from several countries.

In 1990, responsibility for the continuing development of the curriculum frameworks for both mathematics and science was assigned to the Survey of Science and Mathematics Opportunity (SMSO) project under the leadership of Bill Schmidt of Michigan State University. Leigh Burstein, Curtis McKnight, Senta Raizen, Bill Schmidt, Jane Swafford, David Wiley, Richard Wolfe, and I were involved at that stage and in the characterization of the frameworks as "multi-aspect, multi-category systems." Funding for SMSO was provided by the U.S. National Center for Education Statistics and the National Science Foundation.

The first formal international review of the frameworks took place in the context of a conference sponsored by the U.S. National Center for Education Statistics in May 1991 in Washington, D.C. At that meeting, two working groups—one consisting of mathematics educators from several countries, and the other of science educators— spent two days analyzing and commenting on each framework as it then existed.

Additional input on the structure and content of the frameworks was provided by Geoffrey Howson, as well as by many of the TIMSS national project coordinators and their national committees. More international comments and suggestions were received in the context of a conference on the topic of evaluation sponsored by the International Commission on Mathematical Instruction in Calonge, Spain in the spring of 1991.

The frameworks are an excellent example of the kind of work that the International Association for the Evaluation of Educational Achievement (IEA) is capable of. The frameworks represent a consensus developed among many individuals and groups, each seeking the best way possible to communicate information about science and mathematics curricula in a mutually understandable and highly useful way. On behalf of everyone involved in TIMSS, I wish to extend my thanks to all those who played a role in the development process. They have contributed to the success of the study in a significant way.

David F. Robitaille
International Coordinator
Vancouver, 1993

Chapter 1

An Introduction to TIMSS

We believe ... that an understanding of a foreign [educational] system can illuminate one's own.... [1]

The Third International Mathematics and Science Study (TIMSS) is the latest and most ambitious study to be undertaken by the International Association for the Evaluation of Educational Achievement (IEA). IEA has been conducting international, comparative studies of education for over thirty years and, in that time, the organization has developed a well-deserved reputation for excellence and expertise in the area. IEA's previous studies of mathematics and science resulted in a number of significant findings that countries around the world have utilized in their efforts to improve the teaching and learning of mathematics and science in their schools.

Instrument development, piloting, data collection, analysis, and reporting for TIMSS will occur in two phases over the next several years, with research on the findings continuing into the next decade. Major reports and publications are scheduled to appear throughout the lifetime of the project.

More than 50 educational systems have indicated their intention of participating in one or more aspects of TIMSS and it is estimated that over 500 000 students and their teachers will take part in Phase 1 of the study. Data collection at the student level for Phase 1 is scheduled for the 1994–1995 school year, with the first international report of those results expected to be published in the third quarter of 1996. Phase 2 will begin that same year, with student-level data collection in 1998–99 and international reporting in 2000.

The International Association for the Evaluation of Educational Achievement

The International Association for the Evaluation of Educational Achievement (IEA) was established in 1960 as a consortium of educational research centres from about fifteen countries, with Professor Torsten Husén of Sweden as the founding chairperson. The primary goals of IEA are to conduct cooperative international research studies in education and to contribute to the development of research expertise worldwide. IEA is chartered in Belgium and its headquarters are located in The Hague. The chairperson of the organization is Professor Tjeerd Plomp of Twente University in the Netherlands, and the Executive Director is Dr. William Loxley.

Since its first study in the early 1960s, IEA has conducted a number of major international studies and has grown to include over 50 members. In addition to the mathematics and science studies discussed in this monograph, IEA has recently conducted, or is currently in the process of conducting, studies on classroom environment, written composition, reading literacy, pre-primary education, and computers in education.

The countries and jurisdictions with educational systems that have expressed an interest in participating in the project are listed below.

Argentina	Dominican	Japan	Slovak Republic
Australia	Republic	Korea	Slovenia
Austria	Ecuador	Kuwait	Spain
Belgium	England	Latvia	Sweden
Bulgaria	Estonia	Lithuania	Switzerland
Canada	France	Mexico	Thailand
Chile	Germany	Netherlands	Tunisia
China	Greece	New Zealand	United States of
Chinese	Hong Kong	Norway	America
Taipei	Hungary	Portugal	Zimbabwe
Colombia	Indonesia	Romania	
Costa Rica	Iran	Russian	
Cyprus	Ireland	Federation	
Czech Republic	Israel	Scotland	
Denmark	Italy	Singapore	

Explaining Differences Among Educational Systems

Research [on curriculum] contributes by informing the decisions faced in practice, informing them not only with specific facts but also with ways of perceiving curricular situations, thinking about them, and acting on them.[2]

One of the hallmarks of IEA studies, and certainly of the more recent ones, has been the recognition given to the importance of curriculum as a variable in explaining differences among national school systems and in accounting for differences among student outcomes. To understand educational systems and to be able to draw valid comparisons among them, information about curriculum and about instructional practices must be available along with data on student outcomes. These three factors—curriculum, instructional practices, and student outcomes—are the three central points that characterize and help explain national systems of mathematics and science education.

Thus, TIMSS has three major foci: an in-depth analysis of mathematics and science curricula, an investigation of instructional practices based mainly on teacher self-report data, and an assessment of students' mastery of the curriculum as well as their attitudes and opinions. There seems to be little point in ranking countries on some measure of achievement—even if there were universal agreement on the validity of the scale to be employed—unless the resulting differences can be explained in terms of variations in curriculum, instructional practices, or some other variables. That kind of explanatory material can be used by countries to evaluate their own curricula in the light of the outcomes achieved by their students and to suggest directions in which curriculum reform might be directed.

IEA studies have always been conducted with a desire to know the "why's" of the outcomes. As a result, the reports of these studies have avoided competitive metaphors that imply such studies are not "horse races" or "academic Olympiads." In recent years, however, there have been frequent cries for educational reform, especially in mathematics and science education, in many countries. Often these demands for reform have been couched in terms of economic competitiveness in an increasingly interdependent world marketplace.

The effectiveness of some curricula are such that they meet "world-class" standards in producing an educated citizenry, in providing their country with the human capital deemed essential for economic competitiveness, and so on. The explanatory potential for a study such as TIMSS can be used to describe "what works" in terms of curriculum information from around the world, thereby contributing to the development of standards for "world-class" curricula.

TIMSS Curriculum Frameworks

A comparative dimension may make some things previously deemed routine more problematical and thus perhaps in need of either reexamination ... on the one hand or reform on the other.[3]

The development of the TIMSS curriculum frameworks for mathematics and science was an essential first step in the study. The frameworks have served as guides for the design of the achievement testing component of TIMSS, and as the foundation upon which the curriculum analysis component of the study is based. As entities in their own right, the frameworks portray the structure of school mathematics and science curricula, and provide a powerful analytic tool for comparing and contrasting curricula from different countries. A major challenge that had to be faced in developing these frameworks was to ensure that they would remain valid throughout the lifetime of the project. This means that it was not only necessary that the frameworks be valid for describing and characterizing science and mathematics curricula of the present and recent past, they also had to be useful for tracking changes in curriculum over the next several years.

The goal of this monograph is to explicate those frameworks, to trace the process of their development as part of the overall TIMSS project, and to show where the frameworks and the curriculum analysis fit into the study as a whole. Chapter 2 contains an overview of the study as a whole, as well as a description of the conceptual framework and related research questions. Chapter 3 includes a description of the structure of the frameworks and presents some suggestions about ways in which the frameworks might be used to provide rich descriptions of student outcome data. The frameworks themselves are presented in the appendices.

TIMSS will be the largest international survey of mathematics and science education ever conducted, and it is scheduled to continue throughout the 1990s. We believe that the curriculum analysis will be one of the most significant and influential components of the entire project. We also believe that the frameworks themselves will be seen as a major contribution to the fields of curriculum development and curriculum analysis internationally. Evidence of that influence has already been seen in some science curriculum work presently being carried out by the United Nations Educational Scientific and Cultural Organization (UNESCO).

Notes

1. Griffiths, H.B., and Howson, A.G. (1974). *Mathematics, society and curricula*. Cambridge: Cambridge University Press.
2. Walker, D.F. (1992). Methodological issues in curriculum research. In Jackson, P.W. (Ed.), *Handbook of research on curriculum*. New York: Macmillan Publishing.
3. Nicholas, E.J. (1980). A comparative view of curriculum development. In A.V. Kelly (Ed.), *Curriculum context*. London: Harper and Row.

Chapter 2

TIMSS and Cross-National Comparisons in Education

... the educational system is one of the main vehicles for a society's social and economic reproduction.... It provides a means of increasing capital assets—by, for example, the expansion of the economy through investment in trained manpower.[1]

The interest that governments around the world have shown in assessing what is learned in school reflects a global recognition of the belief that scientific literacy and economic productivity are inextricably linked, with mathematics at the forefront as the universal language of modern technology (Walberg, 1983). This provides a powerful economic argument in favour of comparative international assessment in education. Simply put, rising productivity results in a wealthier national economy, which must be continually renewed if that economy is to remain strong and competitive. The failure of a nation to educate its work force threatens that nation's ability to keep pace economically in the international marketplace. The effectiveness of the education system is both an issue and a strategic policy for nations in the global economy (Furino, 1988). Poor school achievement outcomes are commonly found in countries that have poor economic performance. In fact, differences across educational systems are often considered as proxies for differences in economic status and indicators of a country's relative position in terms of global competitiveness.

The international education community looks to the 1990s as a time to strengthen the gains made to date in assessment practices, especially in the evaluation of learning trends over time, and in monitoring the effects of changes in resource allocations to schools. For example, *Education for All*, a conference held in Thailand in 1990 and supported by UNESCO, United Nations Development Program (UNDP), and the World Bank, among others, encouraged less developed countries to undertake national assessments in order to monitor changes in school quality. The Organization for Economic Development (OECD) countries are currently working on a joint initiative to develop educational indicators to track school performance and resource allocations over time. In addition, the European Commission is seeking ways to disseminate standardized school assessment practices throughout Europe, east and west. The 1990s will see a concerted effort to evaluate school achievement world-wide.

The authors of the report of the Second International Mathematics Study (SIMS) in the United States (McKnight *et al., 1987*) coined the expression "underachieving curriculum" to describe a particular situation in the United States with respect to curriculum policy and its effect on students' performance in mathematics. They, along with their counterparts in many other nations, have concluded that their schools must bring ever greater proportions of students to higher levels of achievement in mathematics and science because these subjects are of fundamental importance to the technological development and modernization of all countries. The realization that national economies must move forward in the twenty-first century if they are to maintain their competitive stance has profound implications for what is to be taught and learned in schools around the world. To help position itself for the twenty-first century, each country needs pertinent and timely information about how its students and its educational system compare with those in other countries. The assessment and explication of patterns of school learning around the world are precisely what IEA studies are all about.

Not surprisingly given the importance of mathematics in the school curriculum of every country and the universality of much of the mathematics curriculum content, mathematics has most frequently been selected to provide the substantive content of international, comparative studies of education. Some studies—for example, IEA's first mathematics study (Husén, 1967)—used achievement in mathematics as a surrogate for the overall outcomes of schooling. More recent studies, especially IEA's second mathematics study, focused much more directly on international variation in the content of the mathematics curriculum, on the ways in which mathematics is taught, and on broadly defined student outcomes in mathematics (Travers and Westbury, 1989; Robitaille and Garden, 1989; Burstein, 1992; Robitaille and Travers, 1992). Similar developments have taken place in science (Comber and Keeves, 1973; International Association for the Evaluation of Educational Achievement, 1988; Roiser and Keeves, 1991).

The Value of Cross-National Comparisons

Large-scale international surveys are a relatively recent development in the field of educational research. Although such studies can be costly to administer, both in terms of time and resources, the benefits to be derived from them are significant. Identification of the specific factors or combinations of factors that can influence learning is difficult to accomplish because of the complexity of the learning process. A single-country study is also subject to limitations in the number of factors that can be studied, the amount of variability in each factor, and the inter-relationships among them. Conducting a study in the context of different educational systems can lessen these limitations and difficulties and lead to a better understanding of what mathematics and science can be taught and learned, and of the factors that contribute to, constrain, or promote that learning.

Assessing the impact of variables

International studies allow for the investigation of a much wider range of variables than would otherwise be the case. The impact of variables such as class size, age of initial entry into the school system, single-sex

17

schooling, and out-of-school tutoring (Eckstein, 1982) may be difficult, if not impossible, to assess within a single country or educational system. Investigation and analysis of such variables can, however, be done internationally.

Identifying factors that influence learning

International comparisons can help in the evaluation of the impact of different approaches to curriculum and different teaching practices on students' achievement and attitudes. International studies, in Torsten Husén's phrase, use the "world as an educational laboratory," where differing strategies, programs, and practices may help to identify the factors that influence learning. Nations have initiated curricular and school policy reforms based on the analysis of IEA studies, when a comparison of international results indicated the need for review of the national agenda (see citations in Degenhart, 1990).

The educational system within a given country is typically rather uniform with regard to variables such as class size or age of school entry, with the result that it is not possible to exploit the natural variability of those parameters to investigate the extent of their influence within the system. However, by studying the influence of variables across countries, with an accompanying increase in natural variability, one can better examine the implications of alternatives. Hence, the central comparative question each country may well ask is: How do other countries educate their youth differently and with what degree of success? Different approaches to the same goal can be compared and their impact evaluated.

Evaluating educational systems

Findings from international studies can contribute to the overall effectiveness and productivity of a nation's educational system or systems. Accountability in education is of great concern to many societies, to political representatives, and to policy-makers, especially in the present climate of increasingly difficult competition for public funds. Comparisons of student outcomes among countries with similar educational systems can assist those countries in evaluating the performance of their schools and in drawing conclusions about the kinds of changes that appear to be warranted.

In the case of the longitudinal version of the Second International Mathematics Study (SIMS), for example, comparisons were made of mathematics curricula, of teaching practices employed in the teaching of specific topics such as integers or rational numbers, and of streaming or tracking of students. Such studies provide a view of what can be accomplished, a context in which decision makers in each participating country can view their own system. In the Second International Science Study (SISS), comparisons were made of the diversity of curricula at the lower grade levels with the commonality of topics for the senior levels, and further analysis was made of the different paths students could follow in this transition. Findings on the devolution of responsibility for the science curriculum, for the teaching of science, and for the assessment of learning from systems to individual schools and teachers in some countries provided additional useful information for policy makers.

Examining new approaches to teaching

The efficacy of an educational innovation may be evaluated by examining its implementation and operation in another country. New approaches to teaching may be found by examining the classroom practices of teachers from other countries. Stigler and Perry suggest that "cross-cultural comparison also leads researchers and educators to a more explicit understanding of their own implicit theories about how children learn" (1988, p. 199). Without comparisons, we tend not to question our customary teaching practices, and we may not even be aware of the choices we have made in the process of implementing those practices.

Previous IEA studies have reported on cross-national differences with regard to participation or retention rates, the extent of tracking or streaming, gender differences in achievement, the content of the curriculum, and teaching practices. Many of the findings from these studies challenge the conventional wisdom that underlies traditional educational practice and demonstrate that radically different approaches to the teaching and learning of mathematics and science are not only viable, but demonstrably successful. The focus for international studies should be on trying to determine the effects of particular variables on teaching and learning in the context of cross-national comparisons. For example, it is important for North American educators to know that 13-year-old students in France and Japan are not grouped by any measure of ability for instruction in mathematics, and yet their achievement is among the highest internationally.

Determining how opportunity to learn affects achievement

Educational systems differ in the number of learning opportunities made available to students in the system and in the patterns in which these opportunities are distributed to individual students. In previous IEA studies, "opportunity to learn" (OTL) has been shown to be an important variable in accounting for differences in achievement among students from different countries. OTL data can be used to provide suggestions about what students are able to learn at a given age or grade level. Some countries have already used OTL results from previous studies in developing new curricula for their schools. Many of the findings from these studies challenge the conventional wisdom that underlies traditional educational practice.

International studies have also shown that educational systems can retain very large proportions of their age cohorts in the study of academic mathematics or science at the senior secondary level without penalizing the best students. Secondary analyses of the data from previous IEA studies of mathematics and science have shown that the highest ability students from almost all systems perform at about the same level on topics they have all studied. The major differences among the best students appear to be mainly a function of their opportunities to learn.

In sum, a major goal for cross-national studies is to attempt to identify successful curricular and instructional practices among the participating countries: to see what works best and in what context. In this way, all of the participating countries can learn from one another.

The Unfolding Agenda in Cross-National Studies

Although research is needed to determine the kinds of decisions made at societal, institutional, and instructional levels, as well as how those for whom plans are intended are brought into the process, it is obvious that curriculum making occurs at all of these levels.... We do not know very much about these relationships [between levels], except that they exist. Ultimately, one would hope, curriculum inquiry will provide helpful insights into them.[2]

Previous IEA studies of mathematics and science have produced valuable insights into a number of aspects of the teaching and learning process. In addition, they have provided a number of important lessons with respect to the design and conduct of large-scale international research projects in education. As this research has taken place, assessments of its results and methods have led to the unfolding of an agenda for continued research in cross-national comparative studies of mathematics and science education.

TIMSS will build on the foundation of these previous studies and will further the unfolding agenda. It will provide additional information about a number of topics of current interest in the fields of mathematics and science education.

Some of the more prominent needs on the agenda in cross-national studies are listed below:

- Current national and cross-national information that countries can use to compare and contrast their curricula, teaching practices, and student outcomes with those from other countries of interest to them.
- An assessment of the potential impact that alternative curricular offerings, teaching strategies, and administrative arrangements have on student outcomes as evaluated through achievement tests and attitude scales.
- Descriptions of what is possible in the teaching of mathematics and science that broaden the horizons of what is thought possible.

For example, results from SIMS showed that extremely high rates of growth in student achievement were evident in Japan and France. That finding indicates that more significant growth rates might be possible in other countries and that we need to learn how such growth rates are fostered and maintained.

- A better understanding of the importance and the impact of students' attitudes on their learning and of the relationship between the development of positive attitudes and classroom practices. Such an understanding is crucial to the development of a more complete picture of how mathematics and science learning take place, especially in ways that increase both the appreciation of science and mathematics in a nation and the human resources needed in professions requiring scientific and mathematical knowledge.

- Up-to-date information about the extent to which calculators, computers, and other technologies are being used today for instructional purposes, and information about the impact of these technologies on student outcomes. Undoubtedly, the use of calculators and computers for instructional purposes in mathematics and science classrooms in many educational systems has changed significantly since SIMS and SISS were conducted. Such changes need to be documented.

- Current and valid data as the raw material for investigations by educational researchers of many kinds, not only specialists in mathematics and science education. Every aspect of TIMSS—from population definitions, to sampling, to data collection, and data cleaning—will be subject to strict quality control measures to ensure that the results in each country meet international standards for comparability. Educational systems that fail to meet these standards will not have their results included in the international reports of the study.

These needs form only a part of the unfolding agenda for comparative studies in mathematics and science education. Every need described has been considered in the design of TIMSS, and TIMSS has some potential to further the agenda by providing increments of the needed information. International studies usually result in a ranking of participating countries on the basis of their aggregate performance levels on achievement measures. There has been a considerable amount of criticism of the value and the meaning of such rankings, particularly within some sectors of the education community, but there are instances of similar comments from other sectors as well.

Ranking of countries is not a goal of TIMSS; furthering the agenda for obtaining needed information is. Some ranking will be done and some commentators are likely to focus on those rankings almost exclusively. However, within TIMSS the focus will not be on the rankings themselves, but on using the rankings to identify successful curricular and instructional practices that other countries might consider for adoption based on their demonstrated success in other, comparable contexts.

The Timeliness of TIMSS

IEA has established a cycle of studies covering the major areas of the school curriculum: the 1990s will be the TIMSS decade. It has been somewhat more than 10 years since SIMS and SISS were carried out, although publication of most of the international reports from those studies was delayed because of the lack of funding needed to carry out the analyses of the international data. In the interim, interest in cross-national comparisons generally, and in the areas of science and mathematics specifically, has increased dramatically.

Mathematics and science are important components of the school curriculum in every country. They are seen as integral components of every student's educational program—their place in the schools being second only to that of instruction in the national language or languages. As the role and the impact of technology continue to increase in society and in the workplace, the concepts, processes, and skills of science and mathematics are likely to become even more highly valued and the importance of these subjects in school curricula to become even greater.

Many countries around the world are currently involved in major reforms of their curricula in mathematics and science, and many of them will look to IEA and to TIMSS for the kind of information they need to guide that process. In some cases, the pressure for reform may come from a sense of dissatisfaction with reforms adopted over the past 20 years; in others, the goal will be to consolidate gains that have been made during that same period. In every case, however, the national objective will be the same: to provide the students in that country with a "world-class" curriculum to help prepare them and their nation for life in the twenty-first century.

The findings from TIMSS will, therefore, be of great interest internationally to educators, to curriculum developers, to researchers, to policy makers, and to politicians.

Some of the major topics on which TIMSS will report are listed below:

Mathematics and science curricula
The results of the curriculum analysis will document international variation in mathematics and science curricula.

Opportunity to learn
Opportunity-to-learn data, in conjunction with the curriculum analysis, will illustrate what is possible in the teaching of science and mathematics.

Students' achievement
TIMSS will give considerable emphasis to students' achievement, including students' ability to apply their knowledge and skills in non-routine settings.

Use of technology
The role of technology in the teaching and learning of mathematics and science, particularly as regards the use of calculators and computers for instructional purposes, is a topic of significant interest for TIMSS.

Participation rates
The participation of students in pre-university courses in mathematics and science will be examined, particularly with regard to gender-based differences.

Tracking and streaming
There is a considerable amount of international interest in the kinds of practices employed by schools and school systems to direct students' course selection, including tracking and streaming. Information about such practices will be collected at several levels within each participating system.

The role of textbooks
An investigation of the nature, role, and influence of officially prescribed textbooks on the teaching of mathematics and science is one of the main goals of the curriculum analysis component of TIMSS.

Instructional practices
A comparison of instructional practices, based on teacher self-report data, will be a major aspect of the study.

The data from this rich array of cross-national comparisons—involving as it does a large number of widely different countries—should contribute significantly to the unfolding research agenda and to the needs of policy makers, researchers, and educators in many countries.

Conceptual Framework for TIMSS
The conceptual model for TIMSS was derived, in large part, from the models used in earlier IEA studies—especially SIMS (see Travers and Westbury, 1989) and SISS (see Rosier and Keeves, 1991)—modified and updated to meet the particular demands of the present study. Fundamental to the design of TIMSS is the centrality of curriculum as a variable, and the prominence according to the study of curriculum in the project reflects this stance. Also fundamental to the design of the study is the relationship between science and mathematics as separate yet linked components of that curriculum.

As the TIMSS model illustrated in Figure 1 indicates, the educational environment—that is, the sets of variables that impinge on educational achievement—are composed of more than just those variables directly associated with schooling. We know, for example, that the societal context in which the school is situated influences the goals and means of education. The backgrounds of the participants in the school system represent an important set of variables that influence an individual's educational outcomes. Moreover, the actual school system arrangements contribute to the achievement of the students. An appropriate description, therefore, must draw on the important features of the system at all levels, as well as on the societal contexts in which the system operates.

Figure 1. The Conceptual Framework for TIMSS

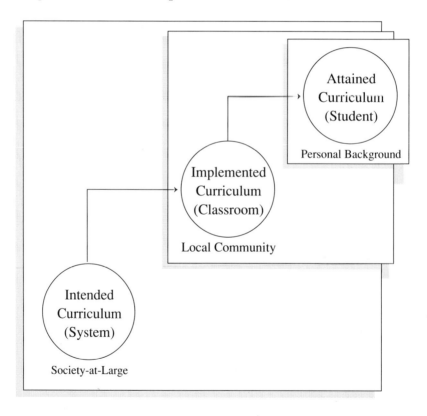

The variety of factors that make up the educational environment can be understood from the perspectives of the three "levels" of curriculum—intended, implemented, and attained—that have been described in previous IEA studies, including the institutional arrangements made for each level of the curriculum and the societal context within which each operates. In the conceptual model of TIMSS, the variables influencing education are seen as situated in a series of embedded contexts starting from the most global and moving to the most personal. The narrow contexts are influenced by the broader ones in which they are embedded, but they are not merely subsets of the broader contexts.

The intended curriculum

The question of who makes curriculum decisions is a fundamental and timeless issue.... The array of participants who are officially designated or who function through default to make curriculum decisions is complex enough, but the question centers around not only who *makes them, but also what type of curriculum decision is under discussion.*[3]

The intended curriculum is the mathematics and science content as defined at the national or the educational system level. The locus of decision making in this regard varies. In some countries, authority may be placed in the hands of many small, local jurisdictions; in others, there may be a highly regulated central authority for a large jurisdiction. Nonetheless, the intended curriculum is embodied in textbooks, in curriculum guides, in the content of examinations, and in policies, regulations, and other official statements generated to direct the educational system. The intended curriculum the mathematics and science students are expected to study and learn may be described in the form of mathematics and science concepts, processes, and attitudes.

The intended curriculum is set within a specific educational context that includes institutional arrangements for the educational system. Educational decisions made at the system level are affected by such features as decision-making structures, and include such decisions as those about school organizational patterns, teaching assignments, and fiscal and human resource allocations.

The intended curriculum is also situated within the larger context of society. The societal context includes those factors that influence system-level institutional arrangements and curriculum content. Illustrative influences from this context are: the goals, expectations, and values society holds for schooling; participation rates; the role of private schooling; the expectations held and the arrangements made for professional preparation of teachers; the professional status accorded to teachers in society; and the resources society has and the proportion of those allocated to education.

The implemented curriculum

Teachers fulfill a variety of functions regarding the creation and implementation of curriculum materials, their curriculum "texts".... The interpretation of curriculum materials allows teachers to express their individual approaches to teaching, as well as their responses to the needs of their specific classroom situation.[4]

The implemented curriculum is the mathematics and science content as it is interpreted by teachers and made available to students. Previous research has shown that the implemented curriculum, even in highly regulated educational systems, is not identical to the intended curriculum. However, the implemented curriculum is influenced by the intended curriculum, and it, too, can be described in terms of concepts, processes, and attitudes.

The implemented curriculum is set in an educational context that consists of institutional arrangements made at the school and classroom level. These are influenced by and, to some extent, depend upon the system-level arrangements. This level of institutional arrangements differs from the system-level arrangements in that the locus for decisions is the school or the classroom. They include such things as teaching practices, aspects of classroom management, use of resources, teacher attitudes, and teacher background.

The implemented curriculum is situated in the broader context of the local community. In some cases, this mirrors society-at-large, and the same features are important. In other cases, however, local communities within an educational jurisdiction vary a great deal. Illustrative features of this context are the social, cultural, and economic factors of the community, expectations held for schooling, and the participation rates of students and parents in community affairs.

The attained curriculum

There are ... potential learners who will respond to something called a curriculum, a curriculum they will perceive quite differently from the way it was perceived by all those who had something to do with producing or developing it. In its movement from wherever it had its beginnings to where these learners encounter it, this curriculum changed profoundly from whatever it was at the outset. To call it a curriculum is a mistake; it was many curricula, each successive one changing more profoundly than a larva changes in becoming a moth.[5]

The attained curriculum consists of the outcomes of schooling—the concepts, processes, and attitudes towards mathematics and science that students have acquired in the course of their schooling years. What students learn will be influenced by what was intended for their learning and by the quality and types of opportunities made available to them.

The attained curriculum is set in the educational context of the individual student and it consists of the institutional arrangements the student makes or has made for his or her own learning—the amount of homework the student does, the effort the student expends, the student's classroom behaviour patterns, and so on. While these factors are greatly influenced by both the system- and classroom-level arrangements, they differ in that the individual student has some direct control over these arrangements.

The attained curriculum is situated more broadly in the context of the student's personal background and is likely to be influenced by societal and community contexts. However, the student's personal context is not likely to be exactly the same as those of others. Thus, it is important to include in the model this additional sphere of influence in order to obtain a comprehensive view. Illustrative of these features are the attitudes about education that students bring to school, their aspirations, their perceptions of their own ability to succeed, parental expectations for their success, and the economic well-being of their families.

The boundaries between the content, the institutional arrangements, and the societal context are not always distinct. Nor is it important that they be clearly delineated. The important point is that the variables of three different kinds of content need to be considered in the light of three different levels of institutional arrangements, within three different societal contexts. Together, the content and institutional arrangements of the intended, implemented, and attained curricula, together with features of the society-at-large, the local community, and the student's own context constitute an appropriate description of the educational environment. It is this conception of the educational environment that guides the design of TIMSS.

Research Questions for TIMSS

For the purposes of this study, curriculum is conceived of as the concepts, processes, and attitudes in mathematics and science that are intended, implemented, or attained. Research questions about the content of curriculum in this multi-level sense are relatively straight-forward: namely, what are the concepts, processes, and attitudes in mathematics and science from the perspectives of each of the three levels of curriculum?

Contextual factors play a role in determining what that content may be, but the dimensions of the interactions are unclear. For example, it is known that the socioeconomic background of a student is correlated with achievement. Many studies have shown that low socioeconomic status is associated with low achievement. It has been hypothesized, however, that low socioeconomic status is only tangentially related to achievement and that a more crucial factor may be the value a student's family places on education or how that translates into a given student's desire to learn. This, in turn, may be associated with, but not determined by, socioeconomic status. Or, it may be that the school is situated in a community of low socioeconomic status, resulting in low expectations for student achievement by teachers; this may be the more important variable for explanation. The point is that we are not certain how variables interact to influence educational attainment.

In a study such as TIMSS, the goal must be to provide sufficient detail to enable a number of different factors to be considered in explaining achievement in different contexts. Sufficient in this case is not some measurable number of details, but the most comprehensive set of details available from an analysis of the various parts of the model outlined in the previous section, from studies previously undertaken, and from the logical deductions of researchers and/or policy makers.

Bradburn and Gilford (1990) suggest that research questions must be selected judiciously. They offer the following criteria: research questions must (a) be relevant to the interpretation of achievement patterns, (b) plausibly relate to school achievement (including locally available educational resources), or (c) reflect additional schooling outcomes valued in their own right.

In addition, research questions in cross-national studies should be selected on the basis of their applicability in the range of cultural contexts of the participants. Answers to the questions must be practicably attainable ("practicable" in terms of accessibility across the various countries and in terms of the time expected of participants in the study), and answers to questions must be ethically attainable (participants must understand the intended use of the data). By considering the three perspectives or levels of the curriculum in their various institutional arrangements and the societal contexts that impinge on them, a number of important research questions can be generated.

Just as there is a blurring of the boundaries of influence between content, institutional arrangements, and societal context, so too there is some blurring of distinction in sources of information. Some aspects of education can be appropriately commented on by students, teachers, administrators, or national-level policy makers. Some aspects are more germane to one group than to the others. International task forces for TIMSS were established to develop questionnaires for all levels and they have been guided by their own critical examination of what is relevant and what is practicable for their respondents.

At the national level, the focus is to collect information about the curricular delivery system. The broad areas of interests include policies, people, instructional materials, and social norms.

At the school level, there are two fundamental research questions: What are the differences within and between countries on selected school characteristics? What is the relationship between selected school characteristics and student achievement within and between countries?

At the teacher level, a synthesis of the research provided by Porter and Brophy (1988), outlines four areas of influence on teachers' instructional practice that focus the research questions: teachers' personal experience and professional education; teachers' development of classroom routines; teachers' planning; and teachers' knowledge and convictions regarding content, pedagogy, and student needs. To these factors must be added concerns about actual instructional implementation, teachers' awareness of systemic policies affecting instruction, teachers' awareness of the goals of the intended curriculum, and teachers' use of textbooks and other materials in instruction.

At the student level, the selection of research foci has been guided by the reviews of relevant literature. In addition, the influence of earlier IEA studies directed the focus of some components of the questionnaires. Primarily, the questions revolve around the availability of parental or home resources, socioeconomic status, and family background as contextual influences on learning. More personally, questions about the centrality of school, future expectations for education, and the value of mathematics and science as perceived by students direct much of this part of the research.

The conceptual model, therefore, provides both a rationale for and a context within which to discuss the research questions that will be the foci of the study. In the most general terms, those research questions are the following:

1. What mathematics and science concepts, skills, and processes have students learned, and what factors are related to students' opportunity to learn those concepts, processes, and attitudes?
2. How do educational systems vary in the intended learning goals for mathematics and science, and what characteristics of educational

systems, schools, and students are related to the development of those learning goals?

3. What opportunities are provided for students to learn mathematics and science, how do instructional practices in mathematics and science vary among educational systems, and what factors are related to this variation?

4. How are the intended curriculum, the implemented curriculum, and the attained curriculum related with respect to the context of education, the arrangements for teaching and learning, and the outcomes of the educational process?

Data Sources for TIMSS

The data used to help answer the TIMSS research questions will come from a variety of sources. These will include questionnaires to be completed by students, by teachers, by principals, and by persons at the national level who are knowledgeable about the educational system or systems within their country. Students will respond to sets of achievement items in mathematics and science, and teachers will be asked to provide opportunity-to-learn information.

The TIMSS data will be obtained from a variety of levels within educational systems and from a variety of sources. Students will provide information about their backgrounds, achievement, opinions, and attitudes, and the same students will provide both the mathematics and the science data. Teachers will provide information about their academic and professional backgrounds, about opportunity to learn, and about instructional practices. Other school-level information will be obtained from principals or department heads.

Data collection from schools, teachers, and students for the TIMSS main study will take place in the second quarter of 1995 in the northern hemisphere and approximately six months earlier in the southern hemisphere.

An in-depth analysis of curriculum will also be carried out. This will include detailed analyses of textbooks and curriculum guides for mathematics and science in each of the participating countries. This curriculum analysis will also help provide contextual information for interpreting analyses in other parts of the study. The reason for employing all of these varied data sources is to provide information about a broad array of factors.

Kinds of Information Sought by TIMSS

- *international variations in mathematics and science curricula, including variations in goals, intentions, and sequences of curricula*

- *international variations in the training of teachers of science and mathematics*

- *the influence of officially prescribed textbooks on the teaching of mathematics and science*

- *the course content that is actually taught in mathematics and science classrooms: i.e., opportunity to learn*

- *the effectiveness of different instructional practices*

- *students' achievement, especially in the areas of non-routine problem solving and the application of science and mathematics in the "real" world*

- *the attitudes and opinions of students and teachers*

- *the role of technology in the teaching and learning of science and mathematics, particularly the use of calculators and computers*

- *participation rates in pre-university courses, with particular regard to gender-based differences*

- *the effect of tracking, streaming, and other practices used to influence or direct students' course selections*

Student Populations in TIMSS

Three age-grade levels of students have been selected as the foci for TIMSS and these are referred to as Population 1, Population 2, and

Population 3. In general terms, Population 1 includes all students in the levels or grades that include almost all 9-year-olds. Population 2 is all students in the grades or levels that include almost all 13-year-olds. Population 3 includes all students in their last year of secondary education, regardless of the kind of program in which they are enrolled and regardless of whether they are currently studying either mathematics or science. Population 3 students who are specializing to some degree in either mathematics or physics have been identified as two subgroups of special interest. Comparison of the performance of these students form part of the TIMSS design.

In the case of Population 3, the population of interest consists of all students who are completing the final year of a program of private or public education including shorter as well as longer programs, vocational programs, and academic programs. For Phase 1 of the study (1995), countries will select the program segment of greatest national interest for their investigation. Results will be reported on a country basis, with the possibility of regional comparisons when comparable segments have been selected. The study will include an investigation of student participation rates in the different kinds of programs available to them. On the basis of this investigation, it will be possible to develop more precise definitions of appropriate segments of this population for Phase 2.

Intended Outcomes of TIMSS

The overall objective of every IEA study is to attempt to provide insights about what students know as well as what kinds of instructional practices, curriculum, and institutional arrangements appear to be associated with high levels of performance. IEA studies are also intended to provide information about the design and implementation of large-scale international studies. TIMSS is no exception to this general rule.

The global objective of TIMSS is to contribute to improvements in the teaching and learning of mathematics and science. Results from the study will provide educators, researchers, and policy makers with the information and analysis they require to make informed decisions about the future of their educational systems.

Measurement of educational achievement

Measuring educational achievement is difficult from both a conceptual and a practical perspective. What counts as "achievement" is not always easy to discern and even when a concept of achievement has been clearly explicated, ways and means for assessing it are not easily devised. The ongoing debate about educational measurement and the increasing number of alternative assessment approaches proposed in educational circles attest to this problem.

Understanding or explaining causes of or influences on achievement is even more difficult. It is one thing to be able to describe what a student knows or is able to do in a given subject; it is quite another thing to explain what might account for that attainment. We know that environmental factors play a large role, yet we are not clear about how that role is played out. The educational context is a complex one, with a myriad of variables interacting with one another in complex ways. In spite of these kinds of difficulties, there are obvious reasons for wanting to assess educational achievement, not the least of which is to try to improve the educational enterprise.

The problems of describing and explaining educational achievement are compounded when considered in international settings. Curricular objectives vary, as do notions of achievement. Educational environments vary immensely. At the same time, an international context is a particularly valuable one for considering the importance of variables that might account for achievement. Studies that cross national boundaries provide participating countries with a broader context within which to examine their own implicit theories, values, and practices. As well, comparative studies provide an opportunity to study a variety of teaching practices, curriculum objectives and structures, school organizational patterns, and other arrangements for education that might not exist in a single jurisdiction.

Being able to describe and explain achievement for countries at different stages of development and with different cultures is dependent upon detailed knowledge of the range of differences. In other words, if comparisons of achievement between and among countries are to be meaningful, a thorough description of a complex set of environmental conditions is crucial, and that description is crucial for at least two different purposes. The first is to provide a detailed backdrop to assist with an understanding of an education system in its particular context. The second is to provide enough detail to permit the isolation of variables that may account for differences in achievement. The challenge facing TIMSS is to describe, appropriately and adequately, different contexts in both the plans for assessment and in the analysis of results.

Objectives of TIMSS and Its Participants

Every participating educational system will have its own particular set of objectives for participating in TIMSS and these will complement those of the project as a whole. All countries will be interested in drawing comparisons between their national educational conditions and accomplishments and those of other countries of particular interest or importance to them. Some countries may decide to use TIMSS as a kind of national program evaluation in the areas of mathematics and science, with a particular focus on how inputs, outputs, and processes vary within the country. In fact, these two possibilities are not mutually exclusive and countries may decide to combine these objectives or add others. That is to say, educational systems may elect to add elements to the basic design of the study in order to meet their particular needs. This kind of flexibility will be available to all participants, given appropriate adaptations of the sample design and instrumentation.

The objectives of the study itself may be characterized in more detail under the headings listed below.

Descriptions of national systems

A great deal of detailed information is needed to construct parallel descriptions of the educational systems participating in TIMSS and to design the samples of schools and classrooms that will participate in the study. National centres will be asked to develop a national case study by completing a number of questionnaires developed for this purpose and by providing data from national and international sources on a variety of factors related to their educational systems.

Descriptions of intended curricula
One of the major activities of the project will be an in-depth analysis and comparison of curricula in mathematics and science. Textbooks, syllabi, and curriculum guides will be analyzed to provide comprehensive descriptions of national intentions for the teaching and learning of mathematics and science internationally. This analysis will include a description of how mathematics and science curricula are differentiated within countries to cater for differing levels of student ability or career choice.

Descriptions of implemented curricula
This analysis will rely primarily on responses to questionnaires by teachers and other school personnel. The goal is to provide rich descriptions of the instructional practices utilized by teachers, the opportunity to learn provided to students, and the instructional resources available for mathematics and science. The questionnaires for teachers will explore in a detailed fashion their intellectual agenda with respect to particular topics in mathematics and science.

Descriptions of attained curricula
For each population participating in the study, a detailed description of students' achievement, opinions, and attitudes will be obtained. The instruments developed to evaluate student outcomes will consist mainly of multiple-choice and free-response items, but will also include a small number of so-called "performance tasks." Both the free-response items and the performance tasks incorporate recent developments and research in the cognitive sciences and assessment.

In summary, a main intention of TIMSS is to provide detailed descriptions of student achievement and to explain variations in such achievement through descriptions of national education systems and their intended and implemented curricula.

Notes

1. Lawn, M., and Barton, M. (1981). *Rethinking curriculum studies*. London: Croom Helm.
2. Goodlad, J. (1979). The scope of the curriculum field. In J. Goodlad *et al.*, (Eds.) *Curriculum inquiry: The study of curriculum practice*. New York: McGraw-Hill.
3. Klein, M. (1991). Introduction. In M. F. Klein (Ed.), *The politics of curriculum decision-making*. Albany, NY: State University of New York Press.
4. Ben-Peretz, M. (1990). *The teacher-curriculum encounter: Freeing teachers from the tyranny of texts*. Albany, NY: State University of New York Press.
5. Goodlad, J. (1979). The scope of the curriculum field. In . Goodlad *et al.*, (Eds.), *Curriculum inquiry: The study of curriculum practice*. New York: McGraw-Hill.

Chapter 3

The TIMSS Frameworks for School Mathematics and Science

Education is a purposeful activity, and the curriculum is the main means whereby the purposes of education are achieved. Therefore, curriculum developers make determined efforts to communicate their own conceptions of the curriculum intentions associated with their projects.[1]

Previous IEA studies have demonstrated the centrality of curriculum as a variable in accounting for differences among student outcomes in comparisons of national systems of education. SIMS and SISS both demonstrated the importance of curriculum for interpreting and explaining differences in instructional practices and student outcomes across countries. In particular, those studies demonstrated that students' achievement is influenced by the opportunity they have to learn particular content and by what content is intended for their learning. For those reasons, TIMSS has as its central focus an investigation of the three levels or perspectives of curriculum— the intended, the implemented, and the attained—as well as the institutional arrangements and societal contexts within which curriculum is delivered.

In order to make valid analyses of curricula and meaningful comparisons of countries with widely different educational environments, a common framework is needed. The TIMSS curriculum frameworks are intended to provide such a structure; and they are being used to characterize curriculum materials, content-specific instructional approaches, and student outcomes.

Thus, the TIMSS curriculum frameworks have two main purposes. First, they are meant to help in the comparison of curricular intentions by providing a common basis for the analysis of curricular intentions and documents that educational systems use to implement their intentions and to guide instruction. Second, the frameworks are meant to provide guidance in the development of appropriate instrumentation for assessing students' achievement and for contextualized discussions of instructional activities.

Development of the TIMSS Frameworks

Earlier IEA studies made use of organizing structures for the analysis of curricula and the construction of achievement measures. These structures have typically been content-by-cognitive-behaviour grids. As Travers and Westbury point out, such a grid was "the bedrock upon which the entire [SIMS] project was built" (1989, p. 16). The widespread use of such grids, at least in the field of mathematics education, has relied to a large extent on the work of Bloom (1956) and, more specifically, on an influential paper by Wilson (1971) in the *Handbook on Formative and Summative Evaluation* (Bloom, Hastings, and Madaus, 1971).

A content-by-cognitive-behaviour grid—sometimes referred to as an "item specification table"—is usually represented as a two-dimensional matrix. The horizontal dimension represents a hierarchy of cognitive behaviour levels at which students may perform, while the vertical dimension specifies particular subject matter topics or areas. Achievement test items or pieces of curriculum are assigned to individual cells, with each item or curriculum piece categorized as representing exactly one level of cognitive behaviour and one element of content. Use of such grids in previous studies has served to provide a common framework for countries to use when describing their curricula, as well as to enable development of fair and equitable achievement items and scales. In addition, these grids provided an organizing framework for analyses of the intended curriculum and its relationship to the implemented and attained curricula.

More recently, critics have charged that such grids have serious limitations and have recommended that alternatives be developed (Romberg and Zarinnia, 1987). They note that use of a content-by-cognitive-behaviour grid fails to take into account the interrelatedness of content or of cognitive behaviours, and that this forces the description of information into unrealistically isolated segments. In addition, questions have been raised about the usefulness of such grids for characterizing curricula and of their flexibility in accommodating different theoretical notions about how students learn.

An organizing framework for the analysis of curriculum needs to be both complex and flexible enough to enable meaningful descriptions of international variations in curricula to be constructed over the almost 10-year duration of TIMSS. Because of the widely recognized limitations of the content-by-cognitive-behaviour grid approach, and the complexity of the design and implementation of TIMSS over several years, it became clear that a different organizational framework was required.

The TIMSS curriculum frameworks were constructed to be powerful organizing tools, rich enough to make possible comparative analyses of curriculum and curriculum change in a wide variety of settings and from a variety of curricular perspectives. The frameworks had to allow for a given assessment item or proposed instructional activity to be categorized in its full complexity and not reduced to fit a simplistic classification scheme that distorted and impoverished the student experience embedded in the material classified.

Structure of the TIMSS Frameworks

The difficulties in making comparisons between mathematics curricula of different countries by examining test items is apparent.... The real problem with the test analysis approach of comparing mathematical curricula is evaluating the appropriateness of the items, the format in which they are presented, and ... the content-by-behavior matrix used to create the items.[2]

For the purposes of TIMSS, curriculum consists of the concepts, processes, and attitudes of school mathematics and science that are intended for, implemented in, or attained during students' schooling experiences. Any piece of curriculum so conceived—whether intended, implemented, or attained, whether a test item, a paragraph in an "official" curriculum guide, or a block of material in a student textbook—may be characterized in terms of three parameters: subject matter content, performance expectations, and perspectives or context. These are the three dimensions or aspects of the TIMSS frameworks (see Figure 2).

Figure 2. The Three Aspects of the TIMSS Frameworks

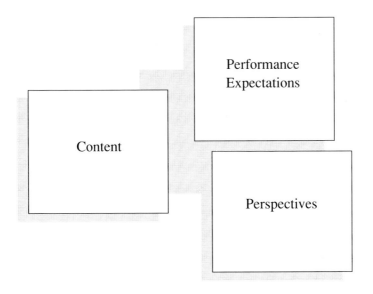

The content aspect is obvious and needs little explanation or development. It represents the content of school science or of school mathematics, depending upon the framework being considered. The performance expectations aspect is a reconceptualization of the former cognitive behaviour dimension. The goal of this aspect is to describe, in a non-hierarchical scheme, the many kinds of performances or behaviours that a given test item or block of content might be expected to elicit from students. The perspectives aspect has particular relevance for analysis of documents such as textbooks, and is intended to permit the categorization of curricular components according to the view of the nature of the discipline exemplified in the material, or the context within which the material is presented.

Each of the three aspects is itself partitioned into a number of categories and sub-categories. However, hierarchies in the case of these frameworks are limited to those within categories, and no hierarchy is to be implied either among the three aspects or among the major categories within an aspect.

Each TIMSS framework may be described as a multi-aspect, multi-category system. What, in the former scheme of constructing content-by-cognitive-behaviour grids, resulted in a strict partitioning of elements into disjoint individual cells in a one-to-one mapping, is very different in the TIMSS frameworks. In the TIMSS frameworks, a test item or block of content can be related to any number of categories within each aspect, and to one or more of the three aspects—thus, the multi-category, multi-aspect designation. It is no longer appropriate to think of disjoint "cells" since the hierarchical levels within a category make overlapping cells possible. An item is no longer represented as a single strand linked to a matrix, and instead may be associated with many combinations of aspect categories in the TIMSS frameworks.

This leads to the notion of a "signature" for an achievement item or for a piece of curricular material. Technically, a signature is a vector of three components and the three components are themselves each vectors of category codes for one of the three aspects of a TIMSS framework. That is, associated with each item or piece of curriculum is an array of categories from one, two, or all three aspects of the relevant framework. Within each of the aspects pertaining to a given item or piece of curriculum several categories or sub-categories may be selected, or one category or sub-category may be selected. The signature reflects the multi-aspect, multi-category nature of the frameworks. It also provides a more realistic depiction of the complex nature of elements of curriculum, and is less reductionist than the traditional one-to-one mappings. It is more suited to the complexity of student activities emerging from the various national reforms of school mathematics and science, and more suited to the rich, integrated performances expected of students in the new forms of assessment that are emerging along with the curricular reforms.

Detailed Structure of the Frameworks

TIMMS is an integrated study of mathematics and science, so the overall structure of both frameworks is similar. Each framework includes the same three aspects: content, performance expectations, and perspectives. The categories within the content aspects are necessarily different for each framework. The performance expectations aspect for each framework consists of five main categories, each with several sub-categories; there is some degree of parallelism between the performance expectations categories of both frameworks. Within this degree of parallelism there are a number of detailed differences, since the arrays of performance expectations have been derived inductively from an examination of curricular materials and curricular reform literature specific to each discipline. The categories of the perspectives aspect are intended to describe the wide variety of attitudes, interests, settings, and applications employed in the two disciplines, and these are essentially the same for mathematics and for science. Each framework represents an array of possibilities for each of the three aspects. Each is intended to represent the range of possible content, performance expectations, and perspectives over the entire span of curricula in mathematics or science from the beginning of schooling through the completion of secondary education. Figure 3, for example, displays the three aspects and major categories for the mathematics framework and Figure 4 does the same for the science framework(see Figures 3 and 4 below).

Figure 3. The Three Aspects and Major Categories of the Mathematics Framework

Content Aspect
- Numbers
- Measurement
- Geometry: position ...
- Geometry: symmetry ...
- Proportionality
- Functions, relations, equations
- Data, probability, statistics
- Elementary analysis
- Validation and structure
- Other content

Performance Expectations Aspect
- Knowing
- Using routine procedures
- Investigating and problem solving
- Mathematical reasoning
- Proportionality
- Communicating

Perspective Aspect
- Attitudes
- Careers
- Participation
- Increasing interest
- Habits of mind

Figure 4. The Three Aspects and Major Categories of the Science Framework

Content Aspect
- Earth sciences
- Life sciences
- Physical sciences
- Science, technology, mathematics
- History of science and technology
- Environmental issues
- Nature of science
- Science and other disciplines

Performance Expectations Aspect
- Understanding
- Theorizing, analyzing, solving problems
- Using tools, routine procedures ...
- Investigating the natural world
- Communicating

Perspectives Aspect
- Attitudes
- Careers
- Participation
- Increasing interest
- Safety
- Habits of mind

The content aspect

The content aspect consists of a breakdown of the subject matter into varying levels of specificity. The content aspect of the mathematics framework is partitioned into ten major categories, each with from two to twenty sub-categories. The science content aspect has eight major categories each with from one to twenty-eight sub-categories.

The task of determining an appropriate number of categories and sub-categories was a challenging one and there is a degree of arbitrariness to the final selection. No doubt other sets of categories and sub-categories could have been used and the choices that were made could be improved upon. Suffice it to say that the categories used in the frameworks were discussed extensively in many international settings and there was a consensus that the ones used in the frameworks were appropriate for the task.

Throughout the development period, there was a good deal of discussion about the degree of specificity needed in the content sub-categories. While narrowly defined sub-categories that would partition the content aspect into a large number of highly specific areas might be useful for some analyses, such an "atomization" of content runs the risk of losing the essential themes of mathematics and science content needed to capture the characteristics of national curricula in other instances.

A case in point would be the differences in approach to the teaching of rational numbers as part of the mathematics curriculum between an educational system that treated decimal fractions earlier in their curriculum than common fractions and another educational system where the reverse was the case. If the more global categories of common and decimal fractions were not present in the mathematics framework, such a major distinction in sequence might be lost. However, if this content was present only at this level of detail, justice could not be done to portraying curricular sequences at a more "micro" level. Furthermore, it would be difficult to portray at all well the curriculum of an educational system that organized its curriculum around such areas as number concepts, operations, and properties but carefully integrated rational number material, represented either as common or decimal fractions. Differing levels of specificity were needed for differing cases and instances. In the end, the desire for varying degrees of specificity had to be provided for in order to make the frameworks applicable in all of the participating educational systems while still preserving the essential structure and content of each subject area.

A major effort was made to ensure that the content categories would be useful for describing trends and changes in curriculum over time. It would not be adequate to have a content aspect that was useful only for describing current or past curricula. The frameworks had to be usable at least for the duration of the study. They had to be designed to make it possible to track emerging trends in curriculum and describe not only traditional topic areas but also areas representing change. Thus, the areas of data representation, probability, and statistics were included in the mathematics framework, and the areas of environmental education and resource issues were included in the science framework. The frameworks need to be able to capture for a decade both the status quo and the status of reforms in both mathematics and science as they occur in over 50 educational systems.

The performance expectations aspect

Processes of inquiry—understanding, investigating, and communicating—are receiving increased international attention as intended educational goals in mathematics and science. The National Council of Teachers of Mathematics, through its publication of the NCTM Curriculum and Evaluation Standards for School Mathematics (1989), has called upon its members in North America and elsewhere to give increased attention to the importance of these processes in the teaching of mathematics at all levels. Similar movements are taking place in science education in a number of countries.

The performance expectations aspect of the TIMSS frameworks describes the kinds of performance that students will be expected to demonstrate while engaged with the content. For mathematics there are five main categories of performance expectations: knowing, using routine procedures, investigating and problem solving, mathematical reasoning, and communicating. For science there are also five categories: understanding; theorizing, analyzing, and solving problems;

using tools, routine procedures, and science processes; investigating the natural world; and communicating.

Each of these categories is subdivided into a number of performance sub-categories that have either an instructional focus (such as goals and objectives presented in textbooks or recommendations about teaching strategies) or a learning focus (such as those typically found in student learning tasks and tasks that sample student performance for formal or informal assessment). The multi-category structure of the frameworks makes it possible to categorize complex, integrated performances because several performance expectations categories can be used to describe a single curricular item. As a result, the frameworks can be used to characterize the performance expectations inherent in any curricular item in either a thematic or an integrated way.

The perspectives aspect

The perspectives aspect of the curriculum frameworks is intended to depict curricular goals that focus on the development of students' attitudes, interests, and motivations in mathematics and science teaching. The perspectives aspect makes it possible to describe learning outcomes or curriculum materials that are intended to promote positive attitudes, as well as goals that encourage students to consider careers in mathematics, science, or technology. Also included are intended learning experiences that promote participation of groups currently under-represented in these fields. In addition, curricular items that are intended to promote scientific and mathematical modes of thought or habits of mind can be described using this perspectives aspect. The five main categories of perspectives in the mathematics framework are attitudes, careers, participation, interest, and habits of mind. The perspectives aspect for the science framework includes the same first five categories, plus safety in experiments as a sixth.

Particular perspectives are not always identified explicitly in textbooks and other kinds of curriculum materials. Instead, textbooks and curriculum guides are frequently constructed to reflect a broad, overall perspective that also covers the content and the performance aspects. However, the nature of the frameworks is such that it is not necessary to categorize every piece of curriculum according to all three aspects. Some pieces will reflect all three aspect, while many will reflect two, and others will reflect only one.

Investigating Curricula Using TIMSS Frameworks

The TIMSS frameworks for mathematics and science were designed to be powerful and flexible conceptual tools for analyzing curricular documents, either of intention or implementation, and for understanding the possibilities and demands of student performance tasks, either for learning or assessment and from the most routine to the most complex.

Analysis of textbooks

> *A textbook is also a surrogate curriculum, that is, a reflection of a sometimes undocumented curriculum that may also be only partially specified. A curriculum is an abstraction, an amalgamation of goals and aspirations. From a single set of curriculum guidelines an infinite number of textbooks could be built, each with its own interpretation of the intent of the guidelines.[3]*

One of the major goals of TIMSS is to provide accurate and timely descriptions of international variations in mathematics and science curricula. As part of that component of the study, the nature, role, and influence of prescribed textbooks on the teaching and learning of mathematics and science will be examined. The TIMSS curriculum frameworks will be the main analytical instruments employed in that investigation.

Manifestations of curricular intentions are ephemeral, but are reflected in myriad ways in the many documents that manifest and guide curriculum. Of these many kinds of documents, one of the most complex and therefore most interesting is the textbook. Textbooks are a bridge from policy documents and the intended curriculum to instructional activities and the implemented curriculum.

To analyze text materials as curricular documents is to look closely at one of the manifestations of curricular intentions closest to the classroom. At the same time, it is to view carefully a document that, at the very least, increases the possibilities of some classroom tasks while lowering the probability of others—that sets out the most common enhancement of a teacher's repertoire and the most common boundary to the learning activities likely to occur in that teacher's classroom.

Sample textbook analysis (1)

The example shown below is from an American eighth-grade textbook, *Exploring Mathematics* (Scott, Foresman and Company, 1991, p. 349).

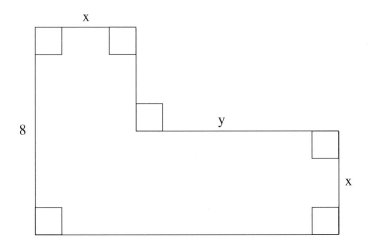

Can you find the area and perimeter of the L-shaped polygon with the information given? If you can, compute it. If you cannot, give reasonable values for the missing lengths needed, and then compute the area and the perimeter.

Using the TIMSS mathematics framework, one would assign content and performance codes for this example (see Appendices A and C). The content codes would include 1.2.2 (perimeter, area, and volume), since these concepts are involved. The content codes would also include 1.1.5.1 (estimating quantity and size), since it is necessary to estimate lengths. The performance codes would include 2.2.3 (using more complex procedures), since estimating activities are part of this category, and 2.2.2 (performing routine procedures), since once estimation is accomplished it is still necessary to compute the perimeter and area of the figure. Finally, they would include 2.3.1 (formulating and clarifying problems and situations) to encompass the decision making involved in deciding that there is not enough information for numerical computation and that estimation must be involved. The nature of the TIMSS mathematics framework as a multi-category system is essential to maintaining the complexity of this problem. No particular perspectives code seems appropriate, so this problem is an example of the fact that a code need not be assigned for all three aspects of a framework.

Sample textbook analysis (2)

A second example is taken from a New Zealand science textbook, *3 Science* (Sweeny, Relph, and DeLacey, 1989, p. 90), written for 13-year-old students.

> *A serving of ice cream contains about 500 kilojoules of food energy, but much more energy than this is used up before we eat it! Describe all the energy used in bringing the ice cream to your table. [Consider energy used in making it, transporting it, storing it. Name the energy form used at each stage if you can.]*

Using the TIMSS science framework, one can describe content and performance codes for this free-response item in the following way (see Appendices B and D). The content codes would include 1.3.3.1 (energy types) and 1.6.5 (food production and distribution methods), since this describes the focus of the problem. The intent of the problem is also to have students describe the history of energy used in bringing ice cream to the table. Therefore a content code of 1.4.3.1 (influence of science and technology on society) would also be appropriate, since this includes the social, economic, and ethical impacts of scientific and technological advances. Performance expectation codes would include

2.1.2 (complex information), 2.4.1 (identifying questions to investigate) and 2.5.1 (accessing and processing information). This problem is also designed to stimulate students' interest in science and technology by engaging them in scientific thought and investigation about a substance that is particularly common to their interests, namely ice cream. Therefore a perspectives code of 3.4 (science, mathematics, and technology to increase interest) would be appropriate. The TIMSS frameworks and its multi-aspects enables a rich description of this open-ended problem.

Analysis of curriculum guides

Recent changes in social and economic conditions, together with the development of powerful new technologies, have far-reaching implications for educational systems. This has led many countries to institute programs of curricular renewal and reform, especially in the areas of mathematics and science. The TIMSS curriculum analysis must be able to capture and characterize the essence of these reform efforts.

The TIMSS curriculum analysis will be one of the most extensive international analyses of the intended curriculum undertaken. Each participating educational system will conduct a content analysis of a selection of their own curriculum documents as well as their textbooks. The selection of curricula to be analyzed depends on the educational system of the country. Countries with centralized educational systems will analyze their national guides and textbooks, and decentralized systems will analyze a sample of regional guides together with a sample of textbooks. Once a country has chosen the materials for analysis, trained individuals will code the content according to the curriculum frameworks.

The policy and intention of any person or institution responsible for curriculum must be communicated to those who will implement that policy and intention. While some communication of curricular intention takes place orally, it is more commonly communicated through various kinds of documents. Those documents most directly concerned with the enactment of curriculum in classrooms might be called "curriculum guides." To describe curricular intentions, either of current or of reform status, the TIMSS frameworks must be able to offer analytic insight into curriculum guides.

Sample curriculum guide analysis

The NCTM (1989) *Curriculum and Evaluation Standards for School Mathematics* is a comprehensive document outlining one possible type of reform in mathematics education. Since many states and districts within the United States have adopted it as part of their curriculum guides, it can serve in some sense as such an example. It contains detailed standards, discussions, and examples for grades K-4, 5-8, and 9-12 in mathematics.

One typical example (NCTM, 1989, p. 27) involves communication in grades K-4.

> *Communicating by talking and listening is also very important. When small groups of children discuss and solve problems, they are able to connect the language they know with the mathematical terms that might be unfamiliar to them. They make sense of those problems. The use of concrete materials is particularly appropriate because they give the children an initial basis for conversation. Such occasions also permit the teacher to observe individual students, to ask probing questions, and to note or attend to any conceptual difficulties individual student might be experiencing. The following discussion activity would help children see how several problems that appear to be different in fact share the same underlying structure: 14 - 5 = n.*

The document then explains that the children would be given counters to model each problem and goes on to outline a classroom activity.

> *With your group, use counters of different colors to model each of these problems and then discuss how the problems are alike or different. [1] Maria had some pencils in her desk. She put 5 more in her desk. Then she had 14. How many pencils did she have in her desk to start with? [2] Eddie had 14 helium*

balloons. Several of them floated away. He had 5 left. How many did he lose? [3] Nina had 14 seashells. That was 5 more than Pedro had. How many seashells did Pedro have?

No framework document can capture by itself the pedagogical variety of this excerpt, but the TIMSS frameworks can be used to describe the richness of these student activities. To code the excerpt above using the TIMSS mathematics framework, the content code would be 1.1.1.2 (whole number operations). The richness of the proposed activities does not lie in its unique content. The performance expectation codes would include 2.1.1 (representing), since central to this procedure is representing real-world situations by concrete and mathematical forms, and 2.3.1 (formulating and clarifying problems and situations), since this is the heart of the activity. It would also include 2.5.2 (relating representations), since the students are explicitly directed to compare the three problems' representations, and 2.5.3 (describing/discussing), as students would be involved in discussing the various representations. Obviously, this characterization of intended student performance is much richer than would be described by a traditional behavioural classification analysis.

Analysis and development of student achievement tasks

One of the other major uses of the TIMSS curriculum frameworks is in the development of appropriate instrumentation for student achievement tasks. The use of the frameworks permits analysis of and provides a frame of reference for the development of test items. The use of the frameworks also provides a common foundation for the interpretation of results of student achievement on those items. It is possible for the test-item signatures to be as complex as the curricular material analyzed; with a multi-aspect, multi-category system the possible combinations of content categories, performance categories, and perspectives categories is virtually endless. The frameworks therefore provide the structure for characterizing existing test items so that they can be viewed in this international context.

Sample achievement task analysis (1)

Many traditional tasks will still be used for some time to come in assessment. The more traditional the task, the less different the TIMSS framework signature will look from more traditional characterizations. For instance, consider the following multiple choice item.

The product of 0.23 and 6.57 is closest to:

a.	*0.0015*	*d.*	*15.0*
b.	*0.15*	*e.*	*150*
c.	*1.5*		

The mathematical content of this task is 1.1.2.2 (decimal fractions), with particular emphasis on operations with decimal fractions. However, since this item is intended to be about the reasonableness and estimation of decimal computations, a code of 1.1.5.3 (estimating computations) would also be used. In a traditional scheme it would be necessary to settle on one or the other of the categories; not so with the TIMSS framework. The performance expectation is meant to indicate what students are expected to be able to do in approaching this task. The intention of this item is to engage students in estimation, but students may choose to answer the problem by computing and rounding off. Therefore, a primary performance code of 2.2.3 (using more complex procedures), which includes estimating to arrive at an answer, would be used to describe the primary intention of solving by estimation. A secondary code of 2.2.2 (performing routine procedures) would then be used to indicate the possible but less preferred alternative approach of solving by computing and rounding. The classification of performance expectation in more traditional schemes would likely be more problematic and the resulting portrait of expected performance less rich.

Sample achievement task analysis (2)

Emerging assessment practice is to use tasks that are more open ended, requiring significant non-routine performance from students and examining the results of that work. One popular name for this approach is performance assessment. A typical task of this sort is one adapted from a recent article (Harel, Behr, Post, and Lesh, 1992).

Given the following diagrams and given that set of blocks B is heavier than set of blocks A, determine which set of blocks C or D is the heavier or if it is not possible to tell. Assume that the blocks in set A and C are the same size and materials, and the blocks in sets B and D are the same size and materials. Give a detailed written explanation of your thinking.

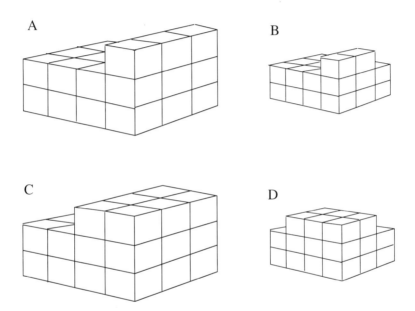

A typical line of reasoning in a solution to this task might go roughly as follows, "There is one fewer block in set B than in set A, but B is still heavier. So each block in A is lighter than each block in B. That means that each block in C is lighter than each block in D. There are the same number of blocks in C and D. So C must be lighter than D."

The mathematical content of this task is less explicit than other tasks, but as demonstrated by this typical solution, the intention is to involve students in some form of proportional reasoning. Accordingly, a content code of 1.5.2 (proportionality problems) could be used. The performance expectation codes would include 2.3.1 (formulating and clarifying problems and situations) and 2.4.4 (conjecturing), since a conjecture about the truth must be determined. In addition, performance codes of 2.4.5 (justifying and proving) and 2.5.3 (describing/discussing) would be included, since a line of deductive reasoning would be used to support the proposition together with a written account of the reasoning involved. This is an example of applying the TIMSS mathematics framework to a very non-traditional performance task.

Analysis of other curricular documents

The analysis of intended curricular documents is just one of the components of the curriculum analysis process using the curriculum frameworks. Topic trace mapping, another component of the process, includes an in-depth analysis of the intended coverage of certain topics throughout the age span from the beginning of primary school to the end of secondary school. The topic trace mapping process, using the curriculum frameworks, will provide TIMSS with important information on international variation in how topics are sequenced in textbooks and curriculum guides and when they are initiated and terminated in the instructional sequence.

A final component of the curriculum analysis process is that of the expert questionnaires. Experts from each participating country will provide information regarding the history of reforms, curricular trends, and policy intentions of how the intended curriculum is to be implemented. The curriculum frameworks will serve as a foundation for the analysis of the intended curriculum through the document analysis procedures, the topic trace mappings, and the expert questionnaires.

Curricula in science and mathematics are manifested not only in texts, tests, and policy documents. They are reflected in many other kinds of documents as well—in the "platform" statements that set out the agendas of educational reforms, in a variety of documents that form the bridge from broad policy to classroom practice and so on. Textbooks and curriculum guides are just two of the latter type of documents.

Another common document of the intended curriculum is an annotated, supplementary "teacher's edition" of a student textbook. Because of the lack of cross-national commonality, documents of this sort are not to be investigated in Phase 1 of TIMSS.

Concluding Remarks

The TIMSS curriculum frameworks are designed to provide rich descriptions of the intended curriculum, ones that can also be used in the development of achievement items. The TIMSS frameworks are powerful organizing structures that are both flexible and sophisticated. The multi-aspect, multi-category nature of the frameworks enables the description of traditional as well as reform-oriented curricula, providing dynamic ways of characterizing curricula internationally. The development of the TIMSS curriculum frameworks has been an extensive endeavour and use of the frameworks in analyzing curricula will help provide new insights into curriculum development internationally.

Notes

1. Heathcote, G., Kempa, R., and Roberts, I. (1991). Curriculum types and strategies. In R. Moore and J. Ozga (Eds.), *Curriculum policy*. Oxford: Pergamon Press.
2. Romberg, T. (1992). Problematic features of the school mathematics curriculum. In P. Jackson (Ed.), *Handbook of research on curriculum*. New York: Macmillan Publishing.
3. Venezky, R. (1992). Textbooks in school and society. In P. Jackson (Ed.), *Handbook of research on curriculum*. New York: Macmillan Publishing.

The Mathematics Framework

This section contains a breakdown of the TIMSS mathematics framework into its main categories within each of the three aspects or dimensions. This is followed by a more detailed breakdown of each category into its sub-categories. Appendix C contains amplified descriptions and a number of examples to illustrate the intended scope of each of the categories and sub-categories.

The Three Aspects
1. Content
2. Performance expectations
3. Perspectives

Major Categories of the Mathematics Framework

Content
1.1 Numbers
1.2 Measurement
1.3 Geometry: position, visualization, and shape
1.4 Geometry: symmetry, congruence, and similarity
1.5 Proportionality

1.6   Functions, relations, and equations
1.7   Data representation, probability, and statistics
1.8   Elementary analysis
1.9   Validation and structure
1.10 Other content

Performance expectations

2.1   Knowing
2.2   Using routine procedures
2.3   Investigating and problem solving
2.4   Mathematical reasoning
2.5   Communicating

Perspectives

3.1   Attitudes towards science, mathematics, and technology
3.2   Careers involving science, mathematics, and technology
3.3   Participation in science and mathematics by underrepresented groups
3.4   Science, mathematics, and technology to increase interest
3.5   Scientific and mathematical habits of mind

Sub-Categories within the Mathematics Framework

Content

The content categories are based primarily on functional considerations. The main goal was to select categories that were useful for coding.

1.1 Numbers

1.1.1 Whole numbers

　1.1.1.1　Meaning

　1.1.1.2　Operations

　1.1.1.3　Properties of operations

1.1.2 Fractions and decimals

　1.1.2.1　Common fractions

　1.1.2.2　Decimal fractions

　1.1.2.3　Relationships of common and decimal fractions

　1.1.2.4　Percentages

　1.1.2.5　Properties of common and decimal fractions

1.1.3 Integer, rational, and real numbers

　1.1.3.1　Negative numbers, integers, and their properties

　1.1.3.2　Rational numbers and their properties

　1.1.3.3　Real numbers, their subsets, and their properties

1.1.4 Other numbers and number concepts

　1.1.4.1　Binary arithmetic and/or other number bases

　1.1.4.2　Exponents, roots, and radicals

　1.1.4.3　Complex numbers and their properties

　1.1.4.4　Number theory

　1.1.4.5　Counting

1.8   Elementary analysis
  1.8.1   Infinite processes
  1.8.2   Change

1.9   Validation and structure
  1.9.1   Validation and justification
  1.9.2   Structuring and abstracting

1.10 Other content
  1.10.1 Informatics

Performance expectations

2.1   Knowing
  2.1.1   Representing
  2.1.2   Recognizing equivalents
  2.1.3   Recalling mathematical objects and properties

2.2   Using routine procedures
  2.2.1   Using equipment
  2.2.2   Performing routine procedures
  2.2.3   Using more complex problems

2.3   Investigating and problem solving
  2.3.1   Formulating and clarifying problems and situations
  2.3.2   Developing strategy
  2.3.3   Solving
  2.3.4   Predicting
  2.3.5   Verifying

2.4   Mathematical reasoning
  2.4.1   Developing notation and vocabulary
  2.4.2   Developing algorithms
  2.4.3   Generalizing
  2.4.4   Conjecturing

Perspectives

Appendix B

The Science Framework

This section contains a breakdown of the TIMSS science framework into its main categories within each of the three aspects or dimensions. This is followed by a more detailed breakdown of each category into its sub-categories. Appendix D contains amplified descriptions and a number of examples to illustrate the intended scope of each of the categories and sub-categories.

The Three Aspects
1.   Content
2.   Performance expectations
3.   Perspectives

Major Categories of the Science Framework

Content
1.1 Earth sciences
1.2 Life sciences
1.3 Physical sciences
1.4 Science, technology, and mathematics
1.5 History of science and technology
1.6 Environmental and resource issues

1.7 Nature of science
1.8 Science and other disciplines

Performance expectations
2.1 Understanding
2.2 Theorizing, analyzing, and solving problems
2.3 Using tools, routine procedures, and science processes
2.4 Investigating the natural world
2.5 Communicating

Perspectives
3.1 Attitudes towards science, mathematics, and technology
3.2 Careers in science, mathematics, and technology
3.3 Participation in science and mathematics by underrepresented groups
3.4 Science, mathematics, and technology to increase interest
3.5 Safety in science performance
3.6 Scientific habits of mind

Sub-Categories within the Science Framework

Content

The content categories are based primarily on functional considerations. The main goal was to select categories that were useful for coding.

1.1 Earth sciences
1.1.1 Earth features
1.1.1.1 Composition
1.1.1.2 Landforms
1.1.1.3 Bodies of water
1.1.1.4 Atmosphere
1.1.1.5 Rocks, soil
1.1.1.6 Ice forms
1.1.2 Earth processes
1.1.2.1 Weather and climate
1.1.2.2 Physical cycles
1.1.2.3 Building and breaking
1.1.2.4 Earth's history
1.1.3 Earth in the universe
1.1.3.1 Earth in the solar system
1.1.3.2 Planets in the solar system
1.1.3.3 Beyond the solar system
1.1.3.4 Evolution of the universe

1.2 Life sciences
1.2.1 Diversity, organization, structure of living things
1.2.1.1 Plants, fungi
1.2.1.2 Animals
1.2.1.3 Other organisms
1.2.1.4 Organs, tissues
1.2.1.5 Cells
1.2.2 Life processes and systems enabling life functions
1.2.2.1 Energy handling
1.2.2.2 Sensing and responding
1.2.2.3 Biochemical processes in cells

1.2.3   Life spirals, genetic continuity, diversity
 1.2.3.1   Life cycles
 1.2.3.2   Reproduction
 1.2.3.3   Variation and inheritance
 1.2.3.4   Evolution, speciation, diversity
 1.2.3.5   Biochemistry of genetics
1.2.4   Interactions of living things
 1.2.4.1   Biomes and ecosystems
 1.2.4.2   Habitats and niches
 1.2.4.3   Interdependence of life
 1.2.4.4   Animal behaviour
1.2.5   Human biology and health
 1.2.5.1   Nutrition
 1.2.5.2   Disease

1.3   Physical sciences
1.3.1   Matter
 1.3.1.1   Classification of matter
 1.3.1.2   Physical properties
 1.3.1.3   Chemical properties
1.3.2   Structure of matter
 1.3.2.1   Atoms, ions, molecules
 1.3.2.2   Macromolecules, crystals
 1.3.2.3   Subatomic particles
1.3.3   Energy and physical processes
 1.3.3.1   Energy types, sources, conversions
 1.3.3.2   Heat and temperature
 1.3.3.3   Wave phenomena
 1.3.3.4   Sound and vibration
 1.3.3.5   Light
 1.3.3.6   Electricity
 1.3.3.7   Magnetism
1.3.4   Physical transformations
 1.3.4.1   Physical changes
 1.3.4.2   Explanations of physical changes

Performance expectations

Perspectives

3.4 Science, mathematics, and technology to increase interest

3.5 Safety in science performance

3.6 Scientific habits of mind

Detailed Mathematics Framework Categories

Content

1.1 Numbers

1.1.1 Whole numbers

1.1.1.1 Meaning (the uses of numbers, place value and numeration, ordering and comparing numbers)

1.1.1.2 Operations (addition, subtraction, multiplication, division, mixed operations)

1.1.1.3 Properties of operations (commutative property, distributive property, etc.)

1.1.2 Fractions and decimals

1.1.2.1 Common fractions (meaning and representation of common fractions, computations with common fractions and mixed numbers)

1.1.2.2 Decimal fractions (meaning and representation of decimals, computations with decimals)

1.1.2.3 Relationships of common and decimal fractions (conversion to equivalent forms, ordering of fractions and decimals)

1.1.2.4 Percentages (all work with percent computations and various types of percent problems)

1.1.2.5 Properties of common and decimal fractions (commutative, distributive, etc.)

1.1.3 Integer, rational, and real numbers

1.1.3.1 Negative numbers, integers, and their properties

1.1.3.2 Rational numbers and their properties (terminating and recurring decimals)

1.1.3.3 Real numbers, their subsets, and their properties

1.1.4 Other numbers and number concepts

1.1.4.1 Binary arithmetic and/or other number bases

1.1.4.2 Exponents, roots, and radicals (integer, rational, and real exponents)

1.1.4.3 Complex numbers and their properties

1.1.4.4 Number theory (primes and factorization, elementary number theory, etc.)

1.1.4.5 Counting (permutations, combinations, etc.)

1.1.5 Estimation and number sense

1.1.5.1 Estimating quantity and size

1.1.5.2 Rounding and significant figures

1.1.5.3 Estimating computations (mental arithmetic and reasonableness of results)

1.1.5.4 Exponents and orders of magnitude

1.2 Measurement

1.2.1 Units (concept of measure and standard units [including metric system], use of appropriate instruments [precision and accuracy], common measures [length, area, volume, capacity, time, and the calendar; money; temperature; mass and weighing; angles; quotients and products of units; km/h, m/s, etc.], dimensional analysis)

1.2.2 **Perimeter, area, and volume** (concepts of perimeter, area, surface area, volume; formulae for perimeters, areas, surface areas, and volumes)

1.2.3 **Estimation and errors** (estimation of measurements and errors of measurement, precision and accuracy of measurements)

1.3 Geometry: position, visualization, and shape

1.3.1 **Two-dimensional geometry: coordinate geometry** (line and coordinate graphs, equation of line in the plane, conic sections and their equations)

1.3.2 **Two-dimensional geometry: basics** (points, lines, segments, rays, angles; parallelism and perpendicularity)

1.3.3 **Two-dimensional geometry: polygons and circles** (triangles; quadrilaterals: their classification and properties; Pythagorean Theorem and applications; other polygons, circles, and their properties)

1.3.4 **Three-dimensional geometry** (three-dimensional shapes and surfaces and their properties; planes and lines in space; spatial perception and visualization; coordinate systems in three dimensions; equations of lines, planes, and surfaces in space)

1.3.5 **Vectors**

1.4 Geometry: symmetry, congruence and similarity

1.4.1 **Transformations** (patterns, tessellations, friezes, stencils, etc.; symmetry [line and rotational symmetry, symmetry in three dimensions, symmetry in algebra and number patterns]; transformations: symmetries and congruence, enlargements [dilations], combinations of geometric transformations, group structure of transformations, matrix representation of transformations)

1.4.2 Congruence and similarity (congruences [congruent triangles and their properties; SSS, SAS], congruent quadrilaterals and polygons and their properties, similarities [similar triangles and their properties])

1.4.3 Constructions using straight-edge and compass

1.5 Proportionality

1.5.1 Proportionality concepts (meaning of ratio and proportion, direct and inverse proportion)

1.5.2 Proportionality problems (solving proportional equations, solving practical problems with proportionality, scales [maps and plans], proportions based on similarity)

1.5.3 Slope and trigonometry (slope and gradient in straight-line graphs, trigonometry of right-angled triangles)

1.5.4 Linear interpolation and extrapolation

1.6 Functions, relations, and equations

1.6.1 Patterns, relations, and functions (number patterns, relations and their properties, functions and their properties, representation of relations and functions, families of functions [graphs and properties], operations on functions, related functions [inverse, derivative, etc.], relationship of functions and equations [e.g., zeros of functions as roots of equations], interpretation of function graphs, functions of several variables, recursion)

1.6.2 Equations and formulas (representation of numerical situations; informal solution of simple equations; operations with expressions; equivalent expressions [factorization and simplification]; linear equations and their formal [closed] solutions; quadratic equations and their formal [closed] solutions; polynomial equations and their solutions;

trigonometrical equations and identities; logarithmic and exponential equations and their solutions; solution of equations reducing to quadratics, radical equations, absolute value equations, etc.; other solution methods for equations [e.g., successive approximation]; inequalities and their graphical representation; systems of equations and their solutions [including matrix solutions]; systems of inequalities; substituting into or rearranging formulas; the general equation of the second degree)

1.7 Data representation, probability, and statistics

1.7.1 Data representation and analysis (collecting data from experiments and simple surveys; representing data; interpreting tables, charts, plots, and graphs; kinds of scales [nominal, ordinal, interval, ratio]; measures of central tendency; measures of dispersion; sampling, randomness, and bias; prediction and inferences from data; fitting lines and curves to data; correlations and other measures of relations; use and misuse of statistics)

1.7.2 Uncertainty and probability (informal likelihoods and the vocabulary of likelihoods, numerical probability and probability models, counting principles, mutually exclusive events, conditional probability and independent events, Bayes' Theorem, contingency tables, probability distributions for discrete random variables, probability distributions for continuous random variables, expectation, sampling, estimation of population parameters, hypothesis testing, confidence intervals, bivariate distributions, Markov processes, Monte Carlo methods and computer simulations)

1.8 Elementary analysis

1.8.1 **Infinite processes** (arithmetic and geometric sequences, arithmetic and geometric series, Binomial Theorem, other sequences and series, limits and convergence of series, limits and convergence of functions, continuity)

1.8.2 **Change** (growth and decay, differentiation, integration, differential equations, partial differentiation)

1.9 Validation and structure

1.9.1 **Validation and justification** (logical connectives, quantifiers ["for all," "there exists"], Boolean algebra and truth tables, conditional statements, equivalence of statements [including converse, contrapositive, and inverse], inference schemes [e.g., modus ponens, modus tollens], direct deductive proofs, indirect proofs and proof by contradiction, proof by induction, consistency and independence of axiom systems)

1.9.2 **Structuring and abstracting** (sets, set notation, and set combinations; equivalence relations, partitions, and classes; groups; fields; linear [vector] spaces; subgroups, subspaces, etc.; other axiomatic systems [e.g., finite geometries])

1.10 Other content

1.10.1 **Informatics** (operation of computers, flow charts, learning a programming language, programs, algorithms with applications to the computer, complexity; history and nature of mathematics; special applications of mathematics [kinematics, Newtonian mechanics, population growth—discrete or continuous models, networks—applications of graph theory, linear programming, critical path analysis, examples from economics]; problem-solving heuristics; non-mathematical science content; non-mathematical content other than science)

Performance expectations

2.1 Knowing
2.1.1 **Representing** (demonstrating knowledge of a nonverbal mathematical representation of a mathematical object or procedure either by selection or by construction, either formal or informal; representations might be concrete, pictorial, graphical, algebraic, etc.)

2.1.2 **Recognizing equivalents** (selecting or constructing mathematically equivalent objects [e.g., equivalent common and decimal fractions; equivalent trigonometric functions and power series; equivalent representation of concepts—e.g., place value; equivalent axiomatic systems; etc.])

2.1.3 **Recalling mathematical objects and properties** (fitting given conditions)

2.2 Using routine procedures
2.2.1 **Using equipment** (using instruments, using calculators and computers)

2.2.2 **Performing routine procedures** (counting and routine computations; graphing; transforming one mathematical object into another by some formal process, e.g., multiplying by a matrix; measuring)

2.2.3 **Using more complex procedures** (estimating to arrive at an approximate answer to a question; collecting, organizing, displaying, or otherwise using quantitative data; comparing and contrasting two mathematical objects, quantities, representations, etc.; classifying objects or working with the properties underlying a classification system)

2.3 Investigating and problem solving

2.3.1 Formulating and clarifying problems and situations (formulate or clarify a problem related to a real-world or other concrete situation)

2.3.2 Developing strategy (develop a problem-solving strategy or data-gathering experiment and discuss that strategy or experiment [not just applying the strategy or carrying out the experiment])

2.3.3 Solving (execute some known or ad hoc solution strategy)

2.3.4 Predicting (specify an outcome [number, pattern, etc.] that will result from some operation or experiment before it is actually performed)

2.3.5 Verifying (determine the correctness of the result of problem solving ; interpret results in terms of an initial problem situation to evaluate how sensible the results are, etc.)

2.4 Mathematical reasoning

2.4.1 Developing notation and vocabulary (develop new notation and vocabulary to record the actions and results of dealing with real-world and other problem situations)

2.4.2 Developing algorithms (develop a formal algorithmic procedure for performing a computation or solving a problem of a certain type)

2.4.3 Generalizing (extend the domain to which the result of mathematical thinking and problem solving is applicable by restating results in more general and more widely applicable terms)

2.4.4 Conjecturing (make appropriate conjectures and conclusions while investigating patterns, discussing ideas, working with an axiomatic system, etc.)

2.4.5 Justifying and proving (provide evidence for the validity of an action or the truth of a statement by an appeal to mathematical results and properties, or by an appeal to logic)

2.4.6 **Axiomatizing** (explore a formal axiomatic system by relating subsystems, properties, or proposition in the system; consider new axioms and their consequences; examine the consistency of axiom systems, etc.)

2.5 Communicating

2.5.1 **Using vocabulary and notation** (demonstrate the correct use of specialized mathematical terminology and notation)

2.5.2 **Relating representations** (work with relationships and related mathematical representations to show the linkages between related mathematical ideas or related mathematical objects)

2.5.3 **Describing/discussing** (discuss a mathematical object, concept, pattern, relationship, algorithm, result, or display from a calculator or computer)

2.5.4 **Critiquing** (discuss and critically evaluate a mathematical idea, conjecture, problem solution, method of problem solving, proof, etc.)

Perspectives

3.1 Attitudes towards science, mathematics, and technology (curriculum encourages positive attitudes towards science, mathematics, and technology)

3.2 Careers involving science, mathematics and technology

3.2.1 **Promoting careers in science, mathematics, and technology**

3.2.2 Promoting the importance of science, mathematics, and technology in non-technical careers

3.3 Participation in science and mathematics by underrepresented groups (curriculum encourages all types of students to study and use science, mathematics and technology; examples of groups that could be targeted: women, racial, and ethnic minorities)

3.4 Science, mathematics, and technology to increase interest (curriculum promotes interest and increasing understanding of topics in science, mathematics, and technology by using experiences that are common to students or popular or intriguing informations; examples include using sports, news, celebrities, history, literature, and interesting data)

3.5 Scientific and mathematical habits of mind (curriculum encourages ways of scientific and mathematical thinking such as openness, objectivity, tolerance of uncertainty, inventiveness, and curiosity)

Appendix D

Detailed Science Framework Categories

Content

1.1 Earth sciences

1.1.1 Earth features

1.1.1.1 Composition (earth's crust, mantle, and core; distribution of metals, minerals)

1.1.1.2 Landforms (mountains, valleys, continents)

1.1.1.3 Bodies of water (oceans, lakes, ponds, bottom of ocean, rivers)

1.1.1.4 Atmosphere (layers of atmosphere [ionosphere, stratosphere, etc.])

1.1.1.5 Rocks, soil (soil types, soil formation, pH of soil, classes of rocks, specific rocks and their uses)

1.1.1.6 Ice forms (glaciers, icebergs, Antarctic)

1.1.2 Earth processes

1.1.2.1 Weather and climate (weather maps, weather forecasts, hurricanes, seasons of the year)

1.1.2.2 Physical cycles (rock cycle, water cycle)

1.1.2.3 Building and breaking (plate tectonics, earthquakes, volcanoes)

1.1.2.4 Earth's history (geologic timetable, formation of fossils, fossil fuels, and mineral resources)

1.1.3 Earth in the universe

1.1.3.1 Earth in the solar system (earth/sun/moon system, night/day, tides, north/south hemisphere, seasons)

1.1.3.2 Planets in the solar system (planets' features, order of planets in solar system)

1.1.3.3 Beyond the solar system (galaxies, black holes, quasars, types of stars, constellations of stars)

1.1.3.4 Evolution of the universe (origin/history/ future of universe)

1.2 Life sciences

1.2.1 Diversity, organization, structure of living things

1.2.1.1 Plants, fungi (types of plants, fungi)

1.2.1.2 Animals (types of animals)

1.2.1.3 Other organisms (types of microorganisms)

1.2.1.4 Organs, tissues(circulatory systems, plant leaf, systems for movement, eyes, ears)

1.2.1.5 Cells (cell membranes, nucleus, mitochondria, vacuoles)

1.2.2 Life processes and systems enabling life functions

1.2.2.1 Energy handling (energy capture, storage, transformation—photosynthesis, respiration, biosynthesis [protein, carbohydrate, fat, etc.], digestion, excretion)

1.2.2.2 Sensing and responding (biofeedback in systems, homeostasis, sensory systems, responses to stimuli [e.g., nervous system and brain])

1.2.2.3　Biochemical processes in cells (regulation of cell functions, translation, protein synthesis, enzymes)

1.2.3　Life spirals, genetic continuity, diversity

1.2.3.1　Life cycles (life cycles of plants, insects, etc.: growth, development, reproduction, dispersal, aging, death; cell division, cell differentiation)

1.2.3.2　Reproduction (plant/animal reproduction, asexual/sexual reproduction)

1.2.3.3　Variation and inheritance (Mendelian/non-Mendelian genetics, quantitative inheritance, population genetics)

1.2.3.4　Evolution, speciation, diversity (evidence for evolution, effects of evolution, processes of evolution [e.g. adaptation, natural selection], nature of a species, domestication, importance of diversity)

1.2.3.5　Biochemistry of genetics (concept of the gene, DNA/RNA, gene expression, genetic engineering)

1.2.4　Interactions of living things

1.2.4.1　Biomes and ecosystems (tundra, rain forest, savannah, wetlands, tide pools)

1.2.4.2　Habitats and niches (habitats of endangered species, niches of species)

1.2.4.3　Interdependence of life (food webs/chains, symbiotic relationships, impact of humans)

1.2.4.4　Animal behaviour (migration of birds, mate selection, rearing of young, social groupings of animals [e.g., beehives, elephant herds])

1.2.5 **Human biology and health.** Note: Many human biology topics will involve double coding. For example, studying the human digestive system (1.2.1.4 and 1.2.5), human impact on the environment (1.2.5 and 1.6), human reproduction (1.2.5 and 1.2.3.2).

1.2.5.1 Nutrition (vitamins and minerals in diet)

1.2.5.2 Disease (disease types, causes, prevention)

1.3 Physical sciences
1.3.1 Matter

1.3.1.1 Classification of matter (homogeneous and heterogeneous materials, elements, compounds, mixtures, solutions)

1.3.1.2 Physical properties (weight, mass, states of matter, malleability of metals, hardness, shape)

1.3.1.3 Chemical properties (periodic table, acidity, reactivity, atomic spectra, organic/ inorganic)

1.3.2 Structure of matter

1.3.2.1 Atoms, ions, molecules (atoms, ions, molecules as the basis for different substances)

1.3.2.2 Macromolecules, crystals (polymers, shape/function of biological molecules, crystal structure)

1.3.2.3 Subatomic particles (electrons, protons, neutrons)

1.3.3 Energy and physical processes

1.3.3.1 Energy types, sources, conversions (potential and kinetic; chemical, nuclear, fossil fuels; hydroelectric power; changing one form of energy to another; energy and work, efficiency)

1.3.3.2 Heat and temperature (temperature scales,

heat as a form of energy, heat versus temperature)

1.3.3.3 Wave phenomena (wave properties, types [e.g., IR, UV], wave interactions)

1.3.3.4 Sound and vibration (transmission of sound, acoustics, harmonics)

1.3.3.5 Light (nature of light, optics, luminosity, reflection, refraction)

1.3.3.6 Electricity (static electricity, electrical fields, alternating/direct current, electrical circuits)

1.3.3.7 Magnetism (magnets and their magnetic fields, magnetic properties). Note: Electromagnetism topics should be double-coded 1.3.3.6 and 1.3.3.7.

1.3.4 Physical transformations

1.3.4.1 Physical changes (gas laws, changes in states of matter, mixing)

1.3.4.2 Explanations of physical changes (general explanations for boiling, freezing, dissolving, etc.)

1.3.4.3 Kinetic theory (kinetic molecular theory)

1.3.4.4 Quantum theory and fundamental particles (quantum nature of light, photoelectric effect)

1.3.5 Chemical transformations

1.3.5.1 Chemical changes (definition of chemical change, types of reactions [e.g., displacement, acid-base, oxidation-reduction, etc.])

1.3.5.2 Explanations of chemical changes (ionic/covalent bonding, electron configurations, electronegativity)

1.3.5.3 Rate of change and equilibria (reagent concentrations, reaction conditions, dynamic equilibrium)

1.3.5.4   Energy and chemical change (activation energy, exothermic and endothermic reactions)

1.3.5.5   Organic and biochemical changes (types of organic compounds, organic reactions, biochemistry)

1.3.5.6   Nuclear chemistry (fission, fusion, isotopes, half-life, mass/energy conversion)

1.3.5.7   Electrochemistry (electrochemical cells/ batteries, electrolysis, oxidation-reduction reactions)

1.3.6   Forces and motion

1.3.6.1   Types of forces (gravitational force, friction, centripetal force)

1.3.6.2   Time, space, and motion (measurement of time, types of motion [linear/rotational], describing motion [constant velocity, acceleration, momentum], reference frames for motion)

1.3.6.3   Dynamics of motion (balanced and unbalanced forces, action/reaction, momentum and collisions)

1.3.6.4   Relativity theory (mass/energy/velocity relationship, explaining the velocity of light, time frames while traveling at the speed of light)

1.3.6.5   Fluid behaviour (hydraulics, Bernoulli principle, pneumatics)

1.4 Science, technology, and mathematics

1.4.1   Nature or conceptions of technology (identifying needs and opportunities, generating a design, planning and making, evaluating)

1.4.2   Interactions of science, mathematics, and technology

1.4.2.1   Influence of mathematics, technology in science (information about contributions of mathematics and technology to development of scientific thought and the practice of science, e.g., new mathematics and technology make it possible for science to investigate new questions or to analyze data in new ways)

1.4.2.2   Applications of science in mathematics, technology (information about contributions of science to development and practice of mathematics and technology, e.g., development of calculus and classical mechanics, industrial processes, types of simple machines, measuring devices— thermometer, Geiger counter)

1.4.3   Interactions of science, technology, and society

1.4.3.1   Influence of science, technology on society (social, economic, ethical impacts of scientific and technological advances, e.g., influence of scientific ideas on social thought, such as social Darwinism; effects of computers on lifestyles)

1.4.3.2   Influence of society on science, technology (information about influence of society on the directions and progress of science and technology, e.g., controversies over research in genetic engineering, use of animals in research)

1.5 History of science and technology (famous scientists, classic experiments, historical development of scientific ideas, industrial revolution, classic inventions)

1.6 Environmental and resource issues related to science

1.6.1 Pollution (acid rain, thermal pollution, global warming)

1.6.2 Conservation of land, water, and sea resources (rain forest, old growth forests, water supplies)

1.6.3 Conservation of material and energy resources (fossil fuels versus alternative energy sources, recycling aluminum)

1.6.4 World population (population statistics, trends; effects of increasing world population, e.g., world hunger, epidemic diseases)

1.6.5 Food production, storage (agricultural methods, food supply and demand, distribution methods)

1.6.6 Effects of natural disasters (environmental damages of hurricanes/typhoons, volcanoes, drought)

1.7 Nature of science. Note: There is a difference between categories 1.7.1 and 3.6.

1.7.1 Nature of scientific knowledge (scientific methods, knowledge subject to verification, knowledge subject to change)

1.7.2 The scientific enterprise (canons of ethics and decision making, professional communication, the scientific community, personnel and processes in large-scale research efforts)

1.8 Science and other disciplines

1.8.1 Science and mathematics (explicit mathematics instruction in the science curriculum)

1.8.2 **Science and other disciplines** (science curriculum incorporated with language arts, social studies, or the arts; examples include chemistry of painting, using art or music to represent or illustrate science concepts, studying the role of science in other cultures, writing stories as metaphors that illustrate science concepts)

Performance expectations

2.1 **Understanding.** Note: The performance expectation is that students will understand the kinds of information in this category. In some materials, the difference between simple, complex, and thematic information may be difficult to distinguish.

    2.1.1 **Simple information** (information such as vocabulary, facts, equations, simple concepts; examples include defining, describing, naming, quoting, reciting, etc.; specific examples are defining scientific terms [boiling point, niche], knowing symbols [abbreviations for units, chemical symbols], describing simple concepts [materials expand when heated, characteristics of animals])

    2.1.2 **Complex information** (information involving the integration of bits of simple information; examples include differentiating, comparing, contrasting, synthesizing; specific examples are understanding how increased external pressure raises boiling point of liquids, how fire is a part of the life cycle of pine trees)

    2.1.3 **Thematic information.** Note: This category should not be coded if students are merely expected to name or describe thematic concepts. (information about concepts with broad applicability that organize and structure knowledge within a discipline or among disciplines; examples include energy, evolution, patterns, change, systems, etc.; a specific example of performance that could indicate understanding of thematic information is using themes to synthesize science knowledge and experiences)

2.2 Theorizing, analyzing, and solving problems

2.2.1 Abstracting and deducing scientific principles (when presented with facts or scientific data, deducing a scientific principle [eg., when presented with spectra of several stars, deducing the stars' relative temperatures; when presented with data on plant growth, deducing that light is required])

2.2.2 Applying scientific principles to solve quantitative problems (using physical laws such as f=ma to solve quantitative problems: when given acceleration [a] and mass [m], calculating force [f]; writing and balancing chemical equations; using balanced chemical equations to answer questions about chemical systems, e.g., stoichiometry problems)

2.2.3 Applying scientific principles to develop explanations (using gas laws to explain changes in gas temperature, pressure, and volume; using ecological principles to predict effect of reducing a population's habitat)

2.2.4 Constructing, interpreting, and applying models (using or creating models that represent systems, objects, events, or ideas: drawing a model of the solar system; making an analogy between human thinking and computer logic)

2.2.5 Making decisions (using scientific skills and knowledge to make decisions regarding personal, local, or societal issues; examples of issues are water purification, nutrition and resource utilization, air quality and energy production; decision making may include defining the decision to be made, identifying alternative choices, weighing advantages and disadvantages of each choice, and committing to action on a particular choice)

2.3 Using tools, routine procedures, and science processes

2.3.1 Using apparatus, equipment, and computers (calibrating an eye dropper, reading a meniscus, using pH paper, folding filter paper, preparing a microscope slide, operating a computer, running a computer program)

2.3.2 Conducting routine experimental operations (measuring the volume of an irregular-shaped solid by displacement of water, conducting a titration, culturing bacteria)

2.3.3 Gathering data (observing, measuring, etc.: perceiving characteristics, similarities, differences, and changes through use of the senses; comparing objects or events to standards of length, area, volume, mass, temperature, force, or time)

2.3.4 Organizing and representing data (classifying, constructing graphs, tables, and diagrams; organizing materials, events, and phenomena into logical groupings; making graphs of data)

2.3.5 Interpreting data (extrapolating or interpolating data from a table or graph, identifying patterns or trends in data)

2.4 Investigating the natural world

2.4.1 Identifying questions to investigate (observing water droplets on outside surface of a drinking glass and forming questions about where the liquid came from; reading about fish dying in local lakes and forming questions about the cause)

2.4.2 **Designing investigations** (developing hypotheses, developing or choosing procedures, selecting materials and equipment)

2.4.3 **Conducting investigations** (executing procedures and recording data) Note: Students are often given prescribed procedures and told the expected results and conclusions. Such investigations are sometimes called "cookbook" experiments, since following procedures is similar to following a recipe in cooking.

2.4.4 **Interpreting investigational data** (organizing data, analyzing data, using data to address investigation's hypotheses or questions)

2.4.5 **Formulating conclusions from investigational data** (using data to make conclusions about the questions or hypotheses of the investigation)

2.5 Communicating

2.5.1 **Accessing and processing information** (finding information, using a library, listening to others for information)

2.5.2 **Sharing information** (reporting work to others, in written or oral form; communicating in a group to solve a scientific problem)

Perspectives

3.1 Attitudes towards science, mathematics and technology

3.1.1 **Positive attitudes towards science, mathematics, and technology** (curriculum encourages positive attitudes towards science, mathematics, technology, and/or the study of them)

3.1.2 Sceptical attitudes towards use of science and technology (curriculum encourages students to evaluate disadvantages of the use of science and technology in society)

3.2 Careers in science, mathematics, and technology

3.2.1 Promoting careers in science, mathematics, and technology (curriculum materials describe or promote careers in science, mathematics, or technology)

3.2.2 Promoting importance of science, mathematics, and technology in non-technical careers (curriculum shows that science, mathematics, and technology are important in automobile repair, accounting, flying airplanes, etc.)

3.3 Participation in science and mathematics by underrepresented groups (curriculum materials encourage all types of students to study and use science or mathematics; examples of groups that could be targeted: women, racial, and ethnic minorities; students in certain regions of a country)

3.4 Science, mathematics, and technology to increase interest (curriculum uses experiences that are common to children as a way of increasing understanding of topics and/ or increasing student interest in topics; popular or intriguing information is used to increase student interest in topics: examples include noting science/math aspects of sports and news, noting celebrities interested in science/math)

3.5 Safety in science performance (curriculum materials describe safe use of materials and equipment, safe procedures)

3.6 Scientific habits of mind (curriculum encourages ways of scientific thinking such as openness, scepticism, objectivity, tolerance of uncertainty, and curiosity)

References

Ben-Peretz, M. (1990). The teacher-curriculum encounter: *Freeing teachers from the tyranny of texts.* New York: State University of New York Press.

Bloom, B.S. (Ed.). (1956). *Taxonomy of educational objectives: The classification of educational goals. Handbook 1: Cognitive Domain.* New York: Longman.

Bloom, B.S., Hastings, J.T., and Madaus, G.F. (Eds.). (1971). *Handbook on formative and summative evaluation of student learning.* New York: McGraw–Hill.

Bradburn, N., and Gilford, D. (1990). *A framework and principles for international comparative studies in education.* Washington, D.C.: National Academy Press.

Burstein, L. (Ed.). (1992). *The IEA study of mathematics III: Classroom processes in mathematics.* Oxford: Pergamon Press.

Comber, L.C., and Keeves, J.P. (1973). *Science education in nineteen countries.* New York: John Wiley.

Degenhart, R.E. (Ed.). (1990). *Thirty years of international research: An annotated bibliography of IEA publications.* The Hague: IEA.

Eckstein, M.A. (1982). Comparative school achievement. In H.E. Mitzel (Ed.), *Encyclopedia of educational research,* Vol. 1. New York: The Free Press.

Furino, A. (1988). *Cooperation and competition in the global economy.* Cambridge, MA: Balinger.

Goodlad, J. (1979). The scope of the curriculum field. In J. Goodlad *et al.* (Eds.) *Curriculum inquiry: The study of curriculum practice.* New York: McGraw-Hill.

Griffiths, H.B., and Howson, A.G. (1974). *Mathematics, society and curricula.* Cambridge: Cambridge University Press.

Harel, G., Behr, M., Post, T., and Lesh, R. (1992). The blocks task: Comparative analyses of the task with other proportion tasks and qualitative reasoning skills of seventh-grade children in solving the task. *Cognition and Instruction, 9*(1), 45-96.

Heathcote, G., Kempa, R., and Roberts, I. (1991). Curriculum types and strategies. In R. Moore and J. Ozga (Eds.), *Curriculum policy.* Oxford: Pergamon Press.

Husén, T. (1967). *International study of achievement in mathematics,* Vols. I and II. New York: Almqvist and Wiksell, Stockholm.

International Association for the Evaluation of Educational Achievement. (1988). *Science education in seventeen countries: A preliminary report.* New York: Pergamon Press.

Klein, M. (1991). Introduction. In M.F. Klein (Ed.), *The politics of curriculum decision-making.* Albany, NY: State University of New York Press.

Lawn, M., and Barton, M. (1981). *Rethinking curriculum studies.* London: Croom Helm.

McKnight, C., Crosswhite, F.J., Dossey, J.A., Kifer, E.A., Swafford, J.O., Travers, K.J., and Cooney, T.J. (1987). *The underachieving curriculum: Assessing U.S. school mathematics from an international perspective.* Illinois: Stipes.

National Council of Teachers of Mathematics. (1989). *Curriculum and evaluation standards for school mathematics.* Reston, VA: National Council of Teachers of Mathematics.

Nicholas, E.J. (1980). A comparative view of curriculum development. In A.V. Kelly (Ed.), *Curriculum context.* London: Harper and Row.

Porter, A.C., and Brophy, J. (Eds.). (1988). Synthesis of research on good teaching: Insights from the work of the Institute for Research on Teaching, *Educational Leadership, 45,* 74-85.

Robitaille, D.F., and Garden, R.A. (1989). *The IEA study of mathematics II: Contexts and outcomes of school mathematics.* Oxford: Pergamon Press.

Robitaille, D.F., and Travers, K.J. (1992). International studies of achievement in mathematics. In D. Grouws (Ed.), *Handbook of research on mathematics teaching and learning.* New York: Macmillan.

Romberg, T. (1992). Problematic features of the school mathematics curriculum. In P. Jackson (Ed.), *Handbook of research on curriculum.* New York: Macmillan Publishing.

Romberg, T., and Zarinnia, A. (1987). Consequences of the new world view to assessment of students' knowledge of mathematics. In T. Romberg and D. Stewart (Eds.), *The monitoring of school mathematics: Background papers. Vol. 2. Implications from psychology: Outcomes of instruction* (pp. 153-201). Wisconsin: University of Wisconsin-Madison.

Rosier, M., and Keeves, J. (Eds.). (1991). *The IEA study of science I: Science education and curricula in twenty-three countries.* Oxford: Pergamon Press.

Scott, Foresman and Co. (1991). *Exploring mathematics* (eighth grade). Glenview, IL: Scott, Foresman and Co.

Stigler, J.W., and Perry, M. (1988). Cross-cultural studies of mathematics teaching and learning: Recent findings and new directions. In D.A. Grouws, T.J. Cooney, and D. Jones (Eds.), *Effective mathematics teaching* (pp. 194-223). Reston, Virginia: National Council of Teachers of Mathematics.

Sweeny, J., Relph, D., and DeLancey, L. (1989). *3 Science.* New House Publications.

Travers, K.J., and Westbury, I. (1989). *The IEA study of mathematics I: Analysis of mathematics curricula.* Oxford: Pergamon Press.

Venezky, R. (1992). Textbooks in school and society. In P. Jackson (Ed.), *Handbook of research on curriculum.* New York: Macmillan Publishing.

Walberg, H. (1983). Scientific literacy and economic productivity in international perspective. *Daedalus*, 112(2), 1-28.

Walker, D.F. (1992) Methodological issues in curriculum research. In Jackson, P.W. (Ed.), *Handbook of research on curriculum.* New York: Macmillan Publishing.

Wilson, J.W. (1971). Evaluation of learning in secondary school mathematics. In B.S. Bloom, J.T. Hastings, and G.F. Madaus (Eds.), *Handbook on formative and summative evaluation of student learning* (pp. 643–696). New York: McGraw-Hill.